不思議の国のアリス
Alice's Adventures in Wonderland

ルイス・キャロル
著

井上久美
翻訳・解説

Original Illustrations
John Tenniel
•
英文リライト
Anna Udagawa
•
イラスト
©1911/1995/1996 Macmillan Publishers Limited
Licensed by Musashino Kogyo Co.,Ltd.
®MUSASHINO KOGYO CO.,LTD.

不思議の国にようこそ！

『不思議の国のアリス』というタイトルを見た読者のみなさんは、ディズニー映画やハリウッド映画の映像を思い浮かべることでしょう。私もそうでした。

この本に登場するアリスや、アリスが迷い込んでいくWonderland（不思議の国）で出合う生き物たちは、私のイメージとはまったく異なるものでした。

ルイス・キャロル作『不思議の国のアリス』は、ある夏の昼下がり、お姉さんと一緒に川べりで休んでいた小さなアリスが白ウサギを追いかけて穴に飛び込み、不思議の国に迷い込むというストーリーです。英語オリジナル版にはライム（脚韻）や言葉遊びがあふれていて、日本人読書には難解な箇所が多々あります。本書は、すらすらと読める英語と日本語訳、そしてやさしい英語解説を、日本人読者向けに書いたものです。映画では登場しなかった個性豊かな登場人物にも、たくさん出会います。楽しみにしてくださいね。

アリスや読者にとって、"あたり前"ではないことを、あたり前のごとくふるまい、アリスを困らせる連中ばかりが登場します。とまどいながらも、読者はアリスと一緒に、好奇心をそそられ、不思議な世界に知らず知らずのうちに引き込まれていくのです。

作者のルイス・キャロルの本名は、チャールズ・ラトウィッジ・ドジソンで、イギリスのオックスフォード大学の数学講師でした。1862年7月4日（金）のよく晴れた昼下がり、ドジソン先生は、自分が属するクライスト・チャーチ・カレッジの学寮長リドル博士の三人の幼い娘たちと、牧師のロビンソン・ダックワースさんといっしょに、テムズ河の支流を下る舟遊びに出かけました。川下りの間、ドジソン先生は、「ナンセンスなお話を」と次女アリス（当時10歳）にせがまれ、アリスを主人公にしたお話を思いつくままに語りました。『不思議の国のアリス』は、そのときのお話をもとに1865年に出版されたものです。

本書に登場する私が大好きなキャラクターは、海ガメもどきとトカゲのビルです。海ガメもどきはホンモノの海ガメではなく、高価な海亀スープの代わりに使われた牛の頭をしたカメです。大きな瞳にうるうると涙をため、ため息ばかりついています。でも、ロブスターのカドリールダンスをアリスに披露するときの海ガメもどきは、生き生きと跳ねまわります。その豹変ぶりが、せつなく心に響きます。

白ウサギの家では、煙突をガサゴソ下りていくトカゲのビルが、巨大なアリスの足のキックを思いっきりくらい、空中を飛んでいきます。気絶してブランデーを飲まされたビルは、「もうブランデーは十分いただきました。ありがとうございます。おかげで気分が少しよくなりました」と、イヤな役目を押し付けたみんなにお礼を言います。法廷では、女王陛下にインクのつぼを投げつけられ、顔から滴り落ちるインクを使ってせっせと記録に励み、陪審員としての務めを果たそうとします。損な役ばかり押し付けられても文句一つ言わず、もくもくと任務を遂行するビルの姿は、けなげでおかしくて、胸を打ちます。

　誰もが常識はずれで新鮮だから、目が離せません！　どのキャラクターも実に生き生きと描かれています。しまいには、私たちが考える常識って、ほんとうはすっごくおかしなことか……と、考えこんでしまう始末。不思議な世界の魔法にかかったみたいです。

　大きくなったり小さくなったりするアリスは、自分の意思で、萎える心を奮い立たせ、不思議の国を勇ましく探求していきます。出会った不思議な生き物一人ひとりと、実にまじめに、礼儀正しく接します。一人ぼっちで頑張っているアリスが、愛しくて、抱きしめてあげたくなります。

　ひょっとしたら、不思議の国は、わたしたちが今住んでいる世界かもしれません。異文化が同居する地球です。異なる文化や価値観の人たちと心を通わせるためには、アリスのように、心を開いて真摯に接する努力を重ねていかなければなりません。一筋縄ではつながりません。絶対に間違っていると思ったことは、勇気を持って発言しなくてはなりません。

　あなたが知っている人のなかにも、アリスが出会ったキャラクター同様、話が食い違ってしまう人がいませんか？　そんな人を思い浮かべ、不思議の国の住民にあてはめて読み進んでいくことも、楽しいかもしれませんね。

　この原稿を書いている私の隣で、我が家のチェシャーネコ、純白のランちゃんがパソコンの"マウス"の上に乗っかって、私の目をじっと見つめています。あれっ、一瞬、ニヤッと笑ったかのように見えましたが……？

　私たちも幼子のように、無垢な好奇心に目を輝かせ、アリスのように冒険してみましょう。不思議の国はすぐそこに広がっています。

2012年初夏
井上久美

本書の構成

本書は、

　　□ 英日対訳による本文　　　□ 欄外の語注
　　□ セクション毎のフレーズ解説　□ MP3形式の英文音声

で構成されています。

　本書は、「不思議の国のアリス」の英文抄訳と日本語訳を読み進めることで、そのストーリーを楽しみながら、同時にビジネスシーンでも役に立つ英語フレーズも習得できるようになっています。

　会議通訳者として豊富な経験をお持ちの井上久美先生による英語表現解説は、ストーリーの理解を深めるだけでなく、生きた英語表現を身に付けるのに最適です。

付属のCD-ROMについて

本書に付属のCD-ROMに収録されている音声は、パソコンや携帯音楽プレーヤーなどで再生することができるMP3ファイル形式です。一般的な音楽CDプレーヤーでは再生できませんので、ご注意ください。

■音声ファイルについて

　付属のCD-ROMには、本書の英語パートの朗読音声が収録されています。本文左ページに出てくるヘッドホンマーク内の数字とファイル名の数字がそれぞれ対応しています。
　パソコンや携帯プレーヤーで、お好きな箇所を繰り返し聴いていただくことで、発音のチェックだけでなく、英語で物語を理解する力が自然に身に付きます。

■音声ファイルの利用方法について

　CD-ROMをパソコンのCD/DVDドライブに入れて、iTunesなどの音楽再生（管理）ソフトにCD-ROM上の音声ファイルを取り込んでご利用ください。

■パソコンの音楽再生ソフトへの取り込みについて

　パソコンにMP3形式の音声ファイルを再生できるアプリケーションがインストールされていることをご確認ください。
　通常のオーディオCDと異なり、CD-ROMをパソコンのCD/DVDドライブに入れても、多くの場合音楽再生ソフトは自動的に起動しません。ご自分でアプリケーションを直接起動して、「ファイル」メニューから「ライブラリに追加」したり、再生ソフトのウインドウ上にファイルをマウスでドラッグ＆ドロップするなどして取り込んでください。
　音楽再生ソフトの詳しい操作方法や、携帯音楽プレーヤーへのファイルの転送方法については、ソフトやプレーヤーに付属のマニュアルやオンラインヘルプで確認するか、アプリケーションの開発元にお問い合わせください。

目次

不思議の国にようこそ！ 3

本書の構成 5

Part 1 7
Chapter 1–4
　覚えておきたい英語表現 1 66

Part 2 71
Chapter 5–8
　覚えておきたい英語表現 2 148

Part 3 153
Chapter 9–12
　覚えておきたい英語表現 3 226

Part 1

Chapter I-IV

Chapter I
Down the Rabbit-Hole *p. 8*
ウサギの穴に落ちて

Chapter II
The Pool of Tears *p. 22*
涙の池

Chapter III
A Caucus Race and a Long Story *p. 36*
党大会（デタラメ）競争と長いお話

Chapter IV
The Rabbit Needs Little Bill's Help *p. 46*
ウサギのお使い、小さなビル

Chapter I

Down the Rabbit-Hole

Alice was beginning to get very tired of sitting next to her sister by the river and of having nothing to do: once or twice she had looked at the book her sister was reading, but it had no pictures or conversation in it, "and what is the use of a book," thought Alice, "without pictures or conversation?"

So she was thinking (as well as she could because the hot day was making her feel very sleepy) about getting up and picking some flowers when suddenly a White Rabbit with pink eyes ran close by her.

There was nothing *very* strange in that; nor did Alice think it *very* unusual to hear the rabbit say to itself, "Oh dear! Oh dear! I will be

■ get tired of 〜に飽きてしまう   ■ conversation 名会話   ■ as well as she could 彼女はやっとのことで〜した   ■ get up 起き上がる   ■ pick 動 〜を摘み取る   ■ close by すぐ近くに   ■ nor 接 〜もまた〜でない   ■ unusual 形 普通でない

Chapter 1

第 1 章

ウサギの穴に落ちて

　川べりにいたアリスは、お姉さんのそばで何もすることがなく座っているのがとてもたいくつになってきました。お姉さんが読んでいる本を一、二度のぞいてみたけれど、さし絵も会話もありません。「さし絵も会話もない本なんて、なんの役に立つのかしら？」とアリスは思いました。

　そこで、起きあがってお花を摘みに行こうかしらと考え始めました（とは言っても、暑くてすごく眠くなってしまい、一生懸命考えようとしたのです）。突然、ピンクの目をした白ウサギがアリスのすぐそばを駆け抜けていきました。

　それは別におかしなことではなかったし、ウサギが「たいへん、たいへん、遅刻しちゃう！」とひとりごとを言っているのに、ヘンだとは思いませんでした。（でもあとから考えたら、びっくりしても当然なのに、ということに気づ

too late!" (When she thought about it afterwards she realised that she should have been surprised, but, at the time, it all seemed quite natural). When the Rabbit actually *took a watch out of its coat pocket* and looked at it, and then hurried on, Alice decided to get up. She realised she had never seen a rabbit with a coat pocket or a watch. She was very interested in this so she ran across the field after it. She was just in time to see it go down a large rabbit-hole.

Alice went down the hole after it, never thinking about how she would get back out again. The rabbit hole went straight on for some way, and then went suddenly down; so suddenly that Alice did not have time to stop herself falling down what seemed to be a very deep hole.

As she was falling she tried to think what would happen next. First she tried to look down and guess what she was coming to, but it was too dark to see anything. Then she looked at the sides of the hole, and noticed that they were filled with book-cases. She picked up a pot as she passed. It was called "ORANGE MARMALADE," but sadly for her it was empty: She did not want to drop the pot in case it broke and killed somebody, so she put it back into one of the book-cases as she fell past.

■ should have 〜すべきだった(のにしなかった)　■ at the time 当時は　■ take 〜 out of … 〜を…から取り出す　■ just in time やっと間に合う　■ get back 戻る　■ guess 動 〜と推測する　■ in case 〜するといけないから

きました。でもそのときは、なぜかとても自然なことに思えたのでした。）ウサギがなんと、上着のポケットから懐中時計を取りだして眺め、急いで走り去ったとき、アリスは起き上がることにしました。ポケット付き上着を着ているウサギも懐中時計を持っているウサギも、今まで見たことがないことに気づいたのです。すごく興味をひかれ、アリスはウサギを追って原っぱを突っ切りました。ちょうどウサギが、大きなウサギの穴に飛び降りるところを見とどけました。

　アリスはウサギのあとを追って、穴に飛び込みました。どうやって穴からはい上がったらいいのかなんて、まったく考えませんでした。ウサギの穴は、しばらくまっすぐに進んでいて、それからふいに真下に向かっていました。あんまり急だったので、深い穴みたいなところを落ちていくのを止める時間がありませんでした。

　落ちながら、次にいったいなにが起こるのかアリスは考えようとしました。まずは真下を見て、落ちて行く先に何があるのか推測しようと思いましたが、暗過ぎて何も見えませんでした。次に、穴の内側の壁を見てみたら、本棚がぎっしり詰まっているのがわかりました。通りすがりにつぼをひとつ手に取ってみると、「オレンジ・マーマレード」とラベルが貼ってありました。でも残念ながら空っぽでした。うっかり落としてつぼがこなごなに割れて誰か死んでしまったら大変だと思ったので、つぼを落としたくありませんでした。アリスは、落ちて行く途中で、別の本棚につぼをもどしました。

"Well!" thought Alice to herself. "After this I won't be worried about falling down-stairs at home!"

Down, down, down. Would the fall *never* come to an end? "I wonder how far I've fallen," she said aloud. "I must be getting somewhere near the centre of the earth. Let me see: that would be four thousand miles down, I think…" (for you see, Alice had learnt several things like this in her lessons in the schoolroom, and though this was not a *very* good time to practise saying things she had learnt, because there was no one to listen to her, she liked saying it). "Yes, that's about the right distance."

Soon she began again. "I wonder if I will fall right *through* the earth! How strange it will seem to come out among people that walk with their heads downwards! But I shall have to ask them what the name of the country is, you know. 'Please, Ma'am, is this New Zealand? Or Australia?' And what a strange little girl she will think I am for asking such a question! No, I must never ask: Perhaps I will see it written somewhere."

Down, down, down. There was nothing else to do so Alice soon began talking again. "Dinah will miss me very much tonight." (Dinah was her cat.) "I hope they'll remember to give her some milk at tea-time. Dinah, my dear! I wish you were down here with me! But I am afraid there are no mice in the air here." Alice soon began to get rather sleepy—when, suddenly, down she fell on some wood and dry leaves. She had stopped falling.

■ for you see お分かりのとおり ■ no one 誰も〜ない ■ distance 图 距離、隔たり ■ wonder if 〜ではないかと思う ■ right through 〜を突き抜けて ■ downwards 副 下に ■ miss 動 〜がいないのを寂しく思う ■ I am afraid 残念ながら

Chapter 1

「そうね」アリスは思いました。「これからは、おうちの階段を落ちても大丈夫！」

　下へ、下へ、下へ。永遠に落ちていくのかしら？「わたし、どこまで落ちたの？」アリスは大声で言いました。「地球の中心に近づいたに違いないわ。さあと、多分、四千マイルぐらい落ちたんじゃないかしら……」(みなさん、おわかりのように、アリスは学校の授業で、こんなことを勉強していたのです。学習したことを口に出す練習をするタイミングとしてはあまりよくなかったかもしれませんが、誰も聞いていなかったので、アリスは言ってみたくなったのです)。「正解。だいたいそれぐらいの距離ですね」

　またすぐに、「地球を突き抜けてしまうかしら！頭を下にして歩いてる人たちの中に飛び出したら、ほんとうにヘンに思われるでしょうね。でもやっぱり、国の名前を尋ねなくちゃね。『すみません奥様、ここはニュージーランドですか？　それともオーストラリアですか？』そんな質問をするなんて、なんて変わった女の子なんでしょうって、きっと思われるわ。やっぱり質問するのは絶対にダメ。どこかに書いてあるかもしれないし」

　下へ、下へ、下へ。ほかに何もすることがなかったので、アリスはまたひとりごとを始めました。「ダイナは今夜、わたしがいなくてすっごく寂しがるわ」(ダイナは猫の名前です。)「ティータイムにミルクをあげるのを忘れないでほしいわ。わたしの大切なダイナちゃん！　あなたもわたしと一緒に落っこちてくれたらよかったのに。残念ながら空中にネズミの気配はしないけど」アリスは急に、睡魔に襲われました。その時、いきなり、木と枯れ葉の上に落ちたのです。墜落はこれでおしまい。

Alice was not hurt, so she jumped up on to her feet in a moment: She looked up, but it was all dark around her. In front of her was a hallway and she could still see the White Rabbit hurrying down it. She had to move on quickly if she was going to keep following the White Rabbit. So she ran very fast and was just in time to hear it say, as it turned a corner, "Oh my ears and eyes, how late it is getting!" She was close behind the rabbit when she turned the corner, but after the corner she couldn't see the rabbit any more. She found herself in a long, low hall which was lit by some lights hanging from the roof.

There were doors all round the hall, but they were all closed; and when Alice had been all the way down one side and up the other, trying to open every door, she walked sadly down the middle wondering how she would be able to get out of this strange place again.

Suddenly she saw a small three-legged table made of glass; there was a tiny golden key on it, and Alice's first idea was that this might belong to one of the doors in the hall; but, sadly, either the key was too large, or too small. It would not open any of the doors. However, the second time she went along she saw a low curtain that she had not noticed before, and behind it was a little door about fifteen inches high. She tried the little golden key in the lock, and to her great delight it was the right size!

■ hurt 形 けがをした   ■ in a moment すぐに   ■ move on 先へ進む   ■ all round 四方（八方）に   ■ all the way down 端から端まで   ■ belong to ～に属する   ■ either 接 ～か～、または   ■ go along 沿って行く   ■ delight 名 大喜び

Chapter 1

　けがをしていなかったので、アリスはぴょんと立ち上がりました。見上げると、まわりは真っ暗です。目の前には、通路があり、白ウサギが急いで走っていく姿が見えました。白ウサギを追いかけるのなら、急がなくては。超特急で走ると、ウサギが角を曲がりながら、「僕の目も耳も、どんどん遅くなる！」と言っているのがちょうど聞こえました。そのすぐうしろに追いついて角を曲がったのに、ウサギの姿はどこにもありません。低い天井からぶら下がったランプに照らされた、細長い広間にアリスは立っていました。

　広間はドアで囲まれていました。でも全部閉まっていました。部屋の一方から順番にドアを開けようとして広間をぐるりと回りましたが、どれも開きません。がっかりして広間の真ん中に歩いていき、いったいぜんたい、どうやったらこのへんてこな所を抜け出せるのかしらと思いました。
　突然、三本脚の小さなガラス製テーブルがアリスの目に飛び込んできました。その上に、小さな金色の鍵がのっていました。アリスがすぐに思いついたことは、これは広間の扉の一つを開ける鍵かもしれないということでした。でも残念なことに、どの鍵穴にも鍵は大きすぎるか小さすぎて、扉を開けることができませんでした。アリスが二度目に広間を一周したとき、さっきまで気づかなかった背の低いカーテンを発見しました。カーテンのうしろには、40センチぐらいの高さの小さな扉が隠れていました。小さな金色の鍵をその鍵穴に差し込んでみると、うれしいことに、ぴったりはまりました！

Alice opened the door and found that it led into a small hallway, not much larger than a mouse-hole: she sat down and looked along it into the loveliest garden she had ever seen. She really wanted to get out of that dark hall and walk around among those bright flowers, but she could not even get her head through the doorway. Even if her head could get through the hole her body could not. She wished and wished that she could go through that hole because so many unusual things had happened to her that she had begun to think that anything was possible.

There seemed to be no reason to wait by the little door, so she went back to the table, hoping she might find another key on it, or even a book which would tell her how she could get through the doorway in to the garden. A papernote was tied round the bottle with the words "DRINK ME" beautifully printed on it in large letters.

It was alright for the bottle to say "DRINK ME," but Alice was a careful girl. She would not drink it without looking at it first to decide if it would be safe to drink or not. She was careful because she had read several terrible little stories about children who had got burnt, and eaten by wild animals, and other unpleasant things, because they would not remember the simple rules their friends and parents had taught them.

■ look along のぞき込む　■ had ever seen これまで見たことがあった　■ even if たとえ〜でも　■ get through 〜を通り抜ける　■ in large letters 大きな文字で　■ alright ㊟ 結構な、差し支えない　■ get burnt やけどする

Chapter 1

　扉を開けてみると、ネズミの穴ぐらいの小さな通路が向こう側に伸びています。アリスはしゃがんで、のぞき込んで見ると、通路の向こうに、見たことがないようなきれいなお庭が見えました。アリスは、この暗い広間を抜け出して、色鮮やかなお花の中を散歩したくてたまらなくなりました。でも、ドアに頭を通すことさえできません。頭が通ったとしても、体は無理です。アリスは、ドアを通り抜けることができますようにと、一生懸命にお願いしました。だって、普通じゃないことがたくさん起きたから、なんだってありだと、アリスは思い始めたのです。

　小さな扉の前で待っていてもらちがあかないので、アリスはテーブルのところにもどりました。もしかしたら別の鍵が置いてあるかもしれないし、通路から庭に抜けるうまい方法が書いてある本がテーブルの上に置いてあるかもしれません。すると、『アタシヲノンデ』と、大きな綺麗な活字が印刷された紙のメモが結びつけられたビンが置いてありました。

　ビンが『アタシヲノンデ』って言うのは自由だけど、アリスは慎重な女の子です。まずはよく観察して、飲んでも安全かどうか確認して決めなくてはなりません。彼女が慎重なのにはわけがあります。やけどした子どもたちや、野生の動物に食べられた子どもたちや、うれしくない目にあった子どもたちのこわいお話をいくつか読んでいたからです。それはみんな、友だちや両親が教えてくれた簡単な決まりごとを覚えていなかったから起きたことでした。

However, this bottle looked safe and it *didn't* have any signs saying "Dangerous" on it, so Alice decided to try it, and she found it very nice. (In fact, it had a sort of mixed taste of cherry-tart, cooked chicken, and hot buttered toast, so she soon finished it.)

"What a strange feeling!" said Alice. "I must be getting smaller." And she was; she was now only ten inches high. She felt very happy that she was now the right size to go through the little door into that lovely garden. She waited a bit, however, to see if she was going to get even smaller.

After a while, finding that nothing more happened, she decided to go into the garden; but sadly for poor Alice—when she got to the door she found she had forgotten the little golden key, and when she went back for it she found she could not reach up to the table. She could see it quite easily through the glass of the table, and she tried her best to climb up one of the legs of the table, but it was too difficult, and when she was very tired she sat down and cried.

She thought she would seem like a very young girl if she cried so she told herself to stop crying. Soon she saw a little glass box lying under the table: she opened it and found a very small cake in it with the words "EAT ME" on it. "Well, I'll eat it," said Alice, "and if it makes me grow smaller, I can go under the door; so I'll get into the garden whatever happens, and I don't care what happens!"

■ in fact 実のところ　■ get smaller 小さくなる　■ see if 〜かどうかを確かめる
■ after a while しばらくして　■ get to 〜に達する、到着する　■ up to 〜に至るまで
■ try one's best 精いっぱい努力する　■ lie 動 置かれている

Chapter 1

　でもこのビンは安全そうでした。『危険』という標示もついていなかったので、アリスはためしてみることにしました。そしたらとても美味しかったのです（サクランボのタルトと鶏のローストと焼き立てのバター付きトーストの混ざったような味がしたので、ひといきに飲みほしてしまいました）。

　「ヘンだわ！」とアリスは言いました。「わたし、どんどん縮んでいくみたい」本当にアリスは小さくなって、30センチたらずの背になっていました。今のサイズなら、あの小さな扉を抜けて素敵なお庭に出ることができると思い、とてもうれしくなりました。もしかしたらまだもっと小さくなるかもしれないと思って、少し待ってみました。

　しばらくすると、これ以上何も起こらないことがわかったので、いよいよお庭に出てみることにしました。でも、かわいそうなことに、扉の前に行ったとたん、金色の鍵を忘れてきたことをアリスは思い出したのです。それで鍵を取りにもどったら、テーブルの上に手が届かないことがわかったのです。ガラスのテーブルの上に鍵がのっているのがガラス越しによく見えました。テーブルの脚をよじ登ろうとがんばってみたのですが、無理でした。アリスはへとへとになって座りこみ、泣きだしてしまいました。

　ワンワン泣いていたのですが、小さな子どもみたいだと思って、泣きやむことにしました。すぐに、テーブルの下にあるガラスの小箱に気づきました。開けてみると、中には『アタシヲタベテ』と書かれた小さなケーキが入っていました。「わかった。食べるわね」とアリスは言いました。「それでわたしがもっと小さくなったら、あの扉の下をすべりこんで外に出られるわ。いずれにしてもお庭に出られるんだったら、何が起こってもかまわない！」

She ate a little bit of the cake and said to herself "Which way? Which way?" holding her hand on the top of her head to feel which way it was growing, and she was quite surprised to find that she was still the same size. This is what usually happens when one eats cake; but Alice had started to expect unusual things to happen, so it seemed very uninteresting that nothing was changing.

So she started eating, and very soon she had finished the cake.

■ which way どちらに　■ be quite surprised to 〜して非常に驚く
■ uninteresting 形 面白くない、興味の湧かない　■ very soon すぐに

ケーキをちょっとだけかじってから、自分に問いかけました。「どっち？　どっちなの？」アリスは自分の頭に手を置いて、背が伸びているのか縮んでいるのかを確かめようとしました。驚いたことに、まったく変わっていませんでした。ふつうケーキを食べたときにはそういうものなのですが、アリスは、ふつうじゃないことが起こることを期待するようになっていたので、何の変化も起こらなったことはとてもつまらなく思えました。

　そこで、アリスはもっとケーキを食べることにして、あっという間にたいらげてしまいました。

Chapter II

The Pool of Tears

"Curiouser and curiouser!" cried Alice. She was so surprised that she forgot how to speak good English. "Now I'm getting larger. Good-bye, feet." When she looked down she could only just see her feet. They seemed to be such a long way away. "Oh, my poor little feet, I wonder who will put your shoes on now. I am sure *I* won't be able to. You must manage the best way you can—but I must be kind to them," thought Alice, "or perhaps they won't walk where I want them to go! Let me see. I'll give them a new pair of shoes every Christmas." She thought it was a very strange idea to be thinking of giving her feet presents every Christmas.

Just at this moment her head hit the roof of the hall: in fact, she was now rather more than nine feet high, and she at once picked up the little golden key and hurried off to the garden door.

■ curiouser 形 curious（不思議だ）の比較級（本来はmore curiousが正しい用法） ■ I wonder who 一体誰が ■ put ~ on ~を身につける ■ manage 動 何とかやっていく ■ think of 思いつく ■ roof 名 天井 ■ at once すぐに ■ hurry off 急いで立ち去る

第 2 章

涙の池

　「へんてこりんとへんてこりん！」あんまりびっくりしたので、まともな英語を話せなくなってしまいました。「まあ、わたし、どんどん大きくなるわ。あんよさん、さようなら」下を見おろしたら、自分の足しか見えなかったのです。それもものすごく遠くに。「かわいそうなあんよさん、いったい誰があなたたちに靴をはかせてくれるのかしら。わたしにはぜったい無理よ。なんとか自分たちで工夫してね——でもわたしはちゃんと見守ってあげるからね」とアリスは思いました。「そうしなければ、わたしが行きたいところに歩いて行ってくれないかもしれないわ。さてと、毎年クリスマスには新しい靴をプレゼントしてあげましょう」自分の足にクリスマスプレゼントをあげるなんて、ヘンテコな思いつきだと思いました。

　そのとき、アリスの頭は広間の天井にぶつかりました。なんと、3メートル近くにまで背が伸びていたのです。すぐにテーブルの上の小さな金色の鍵をつかんで、庭につながっている扉へと急ぎました。

Poor Alice! The only thing she could do now was (by lying down on one side) look through into the garden with one eye; but there was no hope of her getting through the door so she sat down and began to cry again.

"You shouldn't be crying," said Alice to herself, "a big girl like me shouldn't cry like this. Stop this moment, I tell you!" But she went on crying until there was a large pool of water all round her, about four inches deep and reaching halfway down the hall.

After a time she heard the sound of feet in the distance and she quickly dried her eyes to see what was coming. It was the White Rabbit returning, looking beautifully dressed, with a pair of white gloves in one hand and a large fan in the other. He came along in a great hurry, saying to himself as he came, "Oh, the Duchess, the Duchess! Oh! She will be so angry if I've kept her waiting." Alice felt so worried that she was ready to ask help from anyone, so when the rabbit came nearby she said in a quiet voice. "If you please, Sir…" The Rabbit jumped with surprise, dropped the white gloves and the fan and rushed away into the darkness as fast as he could go.

■ poor 形 かわいそうな　■ a pool of water 水たまり　■ in the distance 遠方に
■ a pair of 一組の　■ Duchess 名 公爵夫人　■ keep someone waiting （人）を待たせる　■ rush away 急いで逃げる

Chapter II

　かわいそうなアリス！　今彼女にできることといったら、（横向きに寝そべって）片目でお庭をのぞきこむことぐらいでした。この扉を抜ける望みは一切断たれてしまったので、アリスは座りこんで、また泣き出しました。

　「泣いちゃダメ！」アリスは自分に向かって言いました。「わたしみたいに大きな女の子がワーワー泣いちゃだめよ。今すぐに泣きやみなさい。これは命令よ！」それでもアリスは泣き続けました。アリスのまわりには大きな涙の池ができました。深さ10センチぐらいで、広間の半分ぐらい広がってしまいました。
　しばらくしたら、遠くから足音が聞こえてきました。アリスはすぐに涙をぬぐって目を凝らしました。白ウサギがもどってきたのです。見事にめかしこんで、片手に白手袋を、別の手には大きな扇子を持っています。おおあわてでこちらに走ってきます。「ああ、公爵夫人が！　公爵夫人が！　お待たせしてしまったら、さぞかしご立腹されるだろう」とぶつぶつ言っています。アリスはすごく不安になっていたので、誰でもいいから助けを求めようと思っていました。だから白ウサギが近づいたとき、アリスは小さな声で話しかけました。「あの、すみませんが……」ウサギはびっくりして飛び上がり、白手袋と扇子を落としてしまいました。そして脱兎のごとく、暗闇の中にかけ去っていきました。

Alice picked up the fan and the gloves, and, as the hall was very hot, she kept fanning herself all the time, and she went on talking. "Dear, dear! How curious everything is today! And yesterday everything happened just as usual. I wonder if I've been changed in the night? Let me think: *Was* I the same when I got up this morning? I almost think I can remember feeling a little different. But if I'm not the same, the next question is 'Who in the world am I?' Ah, *that's* the great problem!"

She began thinking about all the children she knew that were of the same age as herself, to see if she could have been changed for any of them.

"I'm sure I can't be Mabel, for I know all sorts of things, and she, oh, she knows such a very little! Besides, *she's* she, and *I'm* I and—oh dear, how curious it all is! I'll try and see if I still know all the things I used to know. Let me see: four times five is twelve, and four times six is thirteen, and four times seven is—oh dear! I shall never get up to twenty. Let's try something else. London is the capital of Paris, and Paris is the capital of Rome, and Rome—no, that's all wrong. I'm certain! I must have been changed for Mabel! And I shall have to go and live in that little old house and have no toys to play with, and, oh, ever so many lessons to learn! No, I've decided—if I'm Mabel, I'll stay down here! It'll be no use if they put their heads down this hole and say, 'Come up again, dear!' I will only look up and ask, 'Who am I? Tell me that first, and then, if I like being that person,

■ all the time　その間ずっと　■ in the world　(疑問を強調して)一体全体　■ any of them　彼らのうちの誰か　■ used to　以前は〜だった　■ get up to　〜に達する、〜まで行く　■ a toy to play with　遊ぶためのおもちゃ　■ It is no use　〜しても無駄だ

アリスは手袋と扇子を拾い上げました。広間はとても暑かったので、アリスはずっと扇子であおぎながらおしゃべりをしました。「まったく、今日は何から何まで不思議なことばかり！　昨日は何もかもいつも通り。もしかしてわたし、一晩で変わっちゃったのかしら。考えてみましょう。今朝起きたときのわたしは、いつも通りだった？　ちょっと違うような感じがしたように思えてきたわ。でももしわたしがいつもと変わっていたとしたら、次の質問は、『いったいぜんたい、わたしはだれ？』それって大問題だわ！」

　アリスは知っている同じ年齢の子どもたちのことを一人ひとり思い出して、自分がそのうちの誰かに変化してしまったのかどうか考えました。
　「メイベルじゃないことは確かよ。だってわたしはすごい物知りだけど、メイベルは、あの子ったら、ものを知らなさすぎるんですもの。それに、あの子はあの子で、わたしはわたし。それにしても、何もかも不思議すぎるわ！　わたしが知っていることを全部覚えているかどうかためしてみよう。ええっと、4×5は、12ね。4×6は13で、4×7は……まあ大変！これじゃあとうてい20までたどりつかないわ。何かほかのことをやってみよう。ロンドンはパリの首都で、パリはローマの首都で、ローマは……ダメダメ、全部間違い。やっとわかったわ。きっとわたし、メイベルに変えられちゃったんだわ。そして、あの小さな古いおうちに住んで、おもちゃもないところで、たくさんのことをお勉強しなくてはならないんだわ！　いいえ、決めたわ。もしわたしがメイベルに変わってしまったとしたら、ここに永遠に留まるとするわ。みんなが穴の中をのぞき込んで、『いい子だから上がってきなさい！』と叫んでも、わたしは上を見上げてこう言うわ。『わたしは誰？　まずそれに答えて。教えてくれた人がわたしの好きな人だったら、上っていくわ。でもきらいな人だったら、別

I'll come up: if not, I'll stay down here till I'm somebody else'—but, oh dear!" said Alice, starting to cry, "I do wish they *would* put their heads down! I am so *very* tired of being all alone here!"

As she said this, she looked down at her hands and was surprised to see that she had put on one of the Rabbit's little white gloves while she was talking. "How *can* I have done that?" she thought. "I must be growing small again." She got up and went to the table to measure herself and guessed that she was now about two feet high and was still getting smaller: she soon realised that this was because of the fan that she was holding, so she dropped it quickly—just in time to save herself from disappearing altogether.

"That *was* a narrow escape!" said Alice, feeling very afraid about the sudden change, but very happy to find herself still alive. "And now for the garden!" And she ran as fast as she could back to the little door; but it was shut again, and the little golden key was lying on the glass table as before. "Now things are worse than ever," she thought, "for I have never been as small as this before! It's terrible!"

As she said these words, her foot moved, and in another moment she was deep in saltwater. Her first idea was that she had somehow fallen into the sea, "and in that case I can go back by train," she said to herself. (Alice had been to the seaside once in her life, and believed that wherever you go to see the sea in England you find a train station.) However, she soon realised that she was in the pool of tears which she had cried when she was nine feet high.

■ do 助《強調》ぜひ、本当に ■ be tired of ～にうんざりしている ■ and now さて
■ narrow escape やっとのことで逃れること ■ than ever かつてないほどに
■ somehow 副 どういうわけか ■ in that case もしそうなら

の人に変わるまでこのまま下にいるわ』──でも、困ったわ！」とアリスは言って、泣きだしました。「みんな、頭をちゃんと下げてのぞき込んでほしいわ。こんなところにひとりぼっちでいるのはもううんざり！」

そう言いながら、アリスは自分の両手を見おろしてびっくりしました。話している間に、ウサギの小さな手袋が片方だけはまっていたのです。「いったいどうやってはめたのかしら？」アリスは考えました。「わたしって、きっとまた小さくなっているに違いないわ」立ち上がってテーブルのそばに行って背くらべしてみると、身長60センチぐらいに縮んでいることがわかりました。まだまだ小さくなっていきます。アリスはすぐに、それは手にもった扇子のせいだということに気づき、あわてて扇子を手放しました。もうちょっとであとかたもなく消えてしまうところでした。

「あぶなかった！」とアリスは言いました。突然な変化はとてもこわかったのですが、まだこうして生きていることは、とてもハッピーでした。「さあ、お庭に行ってみようっと！」アリスは大急ぎで小さな扉に駆けもどりました。扉はまたしても閉まっていて、金色の鍵はまだガラスのテーブルの上にのったままです。「これじゃあ前よりひどいわ」とアリスは思いました。「だってこんなに小さくなったことは生まれて初めてだもの。ひどすぎるわ！」

そう言いながら、アリスの足が動いて、次の瞬間、塩水につかっていました。とっさに、どういうわけか海に落っこちたのかもしれないと思いました。「だったら、列車でもどれるわ」と、アリスはひとりごとを言いました（アリスは一度だけ海岸に行ったことがありました。イギリスで海を見に行ったら、どこでも絶対に列車の駅があるとアリスは思いこんでいたのです）。でもすぐに、気づきました。アリスが3メートル近くあったときに泣いてできた涙の池にはまってしまったことに。

"I wish I hadn't cried so much!" said Alice, as she swam about, trying to find her way out. Just then she heard something, so she swam nearer to find out what it was: at first she thought it must be a big animal, but then she remembered how small she was now, and she soon realised that it was only a Mouse that had also fallen into the water.

"Would it be of any use now," thought Alice, "to speak to this mouse? Everything is so different down here, that I should think it very likely that it can talk: I'll talk to him and see what happens.

"O Mouse, do you know the way out of this pool? I am very tired of swimming about here, O Mouse!" (Alice thought this must be the right way of speaking to a mouse even though she had never done such a thing before.) The mouse looked at her. He seemed to be interested but he didn't say anything.

"Perhaps it doesn't understand English," she thought. "It may be a French mouse." So she began again. She said "Where is my cat?" in French. They were the first words she had learned in her French lesson-book. The Mouse suddenly jumped out of the water and seemed to shake all over because he was afraid. "Oh, I'm sorry!" cried Alice, afraid that she had hurt the poor animal's feelings. "I completely forgot that you didn't like cats."

"Not like cats!" cried the Mouse in a high voice. "Would *you* like cats, if you were me?"

■ I wish I hadn't ～しなければよかった　■ find one's way out 出口を見つける
■ just then ちょうどそのとき　■ at first 最初は　■ of any use 何かの役に立って
■ shake all over 全身が震える　■ if you were me もし私の立場なら

「あんなにワーワー泣くんじゃなかった！」出口を探して泳ぎまわりながら言いました。そのとき、何か聞こえました。音がする方に泳いでいって、確かめようと思いました。最初、きっと大きな動物に違いないと思いました。でも、今の自分がほんとうに小さくなっていることを思い出しました。そしてすぐに、池に落ちてしまったネズミだってことに気づきました。

「ネズミと話しても意味があるかしら？」アリスは考えました。「ここではなにもかも普通じゃないから、ネズミだって話せるかもしれないわ。とにかく話しかけてみよう」

「おお、ネズミよ、おまえ、この池から脱出する方法を知っている？　わたしもう泳ぎつかれてしまったの。おお、ネズミよ！」（アリスは、これがネズミとの正式な話し方だと思っていたのです。ネズミに語りかけるのは初めてでしたがね）。ネズミはアリスを見つめました。興味を示したのですが、ひとことも言いませんでした。

「英語がわからないのかもしれないわね」と、アリスは考えました。「フランスのネズミかもしれない」さあ、もう一度。「ドコ　デスカ　ワタシノネコ？」と、フランス語で言いました。アリスがフランス語の教科書で最初に覚えた言葉でした。ネズミはあわてて池から飛び出て、こわくてぶるぶると震えている様子です。「まあ、ごめんなさい！」アリスは叫びました。かわいそうな動物の気持ちを傷つけてしまったのではないかと案じて、「あなたはネコが嫌いだってこと、すっかり忘れていたわ」

「ネコが嫌いだって！」ネズミは甲高い声で叫びました。「きみがぼくだったら、ネコが好きになるかい？」

"Well, perhaps not," said Alice in a quiet voice; "but please don't be angry about it. But I wish I could show you our cat, Dinah. I think you'd like cats if you could see her. She is such a dear quiet thing," Alice continued as she swam lazily about in the pool, "and she sits so nicely by the fire, washing her face—and she is such a nice soft thing to look after—and she is very good at catching mice—oh, I am sorry!" cried Alice again, for this time the Mouse was shaking all over, and she felt certain it must be really unhappy. "We won't talk about her any more, if you'd rather not."

"We, indeed!" cried the Mouse, who was shaking all over his body. "As if *I* would talk about such things! Our family always *hated* cats: Don't let me hear the word 'cat' or the name 'Dinah' again!"

"I won't indeed!" said Alice, in a great hurry to talk about something else. "Do you—do you like dogs?" The Mouse did not answer, so Alice continued talking happily: "There is such a nice little dog near our house, I would like to show you it!" But she saw that the Mouse was swimming away from her as fast as it could go.

■ I wish I could 〜できたらよかった ■ swim about 泳ぎ回る ■ look after 〜の世話をする ■ be good at 〜が得意だ ■ would rather not 〜したくない ■ as if あたかも〜かのように

「えーっと、たぶんならないと思うわ」アリスはなだめるような口調で言いました。「でも怒らないで聞いてちょうだい。ダイナちゃんを見せてあげられたらいいのに。ダイナちゃんに会ったら、きっと、あなたもネコが好きになるわ。とってもおとなしくていい子なんだから」池のなかをだらだらと泳ぎまわりながら、アリスは続けました。「ダイナちゃんはね、暖炉のそばにお行儀よく座って、顔をきれいにするのよ。とってもふかふかしていてかわいいこなの――それに、ネズミを捕まえるのがとっても上手なのよ――あっ、ごめんなさい！」アリスはまた叫びました。今度は、ネズミは全身をぶるぶると震わせていました。アリスは、きっと、ネズミをひどく傷つけてしまったに違いないと思いました。「わたしたち、ダイナちゃんのことを話すのはもうやめましょう。その方がいいでしょう」

　「わたしたちだって、まったく！」ぶるぶる震えながらネズミは叫びました。「そんな話題をぼくまでが持ち出すみたいな言い方をして！　われら一族は、先祖代々、ネコどもを憎んできたんだ。〝ネコ〞も、〝ダイナ〞という言葉も、二度と口にしないでくれたまえ！」

　「わかったわ！」とアリスは言いました。あわてて話題を変えようと思いました。「あのー、犬は好き？」ネズミは答えませんでした。アリスはまたうれしそうに続けました。「わたしの家のそばに、とっても素敵な子犬がいるのよ。見せてあげたいわ！」ネズミは一目散に泳いでアリスから遠ざかって行きました。

So she called quietly again, "Mouse dear! Do come back again, and we won't talk about cats or dogs either, if you don't like them!" When the Mouse heard this, it turned round and swam slowly back to her: Its face was quite white, and it said in a low, shaky voice, "Let us get out of the water and then I'll tell you my history, and you'll understand why I don't like cats or dogs."

It was certainly time to go, because the pool was getting quite crowded with the birds and animals that had fallen into it: there was a Duck and a Dodo, a Lory and an Eaglet, and several other curious animals. Alice led the way, and the whole party swam to the shore.

■ either 副 〜も〜もしない ■ shaky 形 震える ■ dodo 名 ドードー《モーリシャス島に生息した大型の鳥、ドジソン（ルイス・キャロルの本名）自身がモデル》 ■ lory 名 ローリー《インコの一種、アリスのお姉さんのロリーナがモデル》 ■ eaglet 名 ワシの子《アリスの妹のイーディスがモデル》 ■ lead the way 案内する ■ party 名 一行 ■ shore 名 岸

アリスはまた、静かに呼びかけました。「ねえネズミさん！お願いだからもどってきてちょうだい。わたしたち、ネコの話も犬の話もするのはやめましょう。あなたがどちらも嫌いなら」　それを聞くと、ネズミは向きを変え、ゆっくりと泳いでアリスのところにもどってきました。顔色はすっかり青ざめていました。そしてネズミは低く震える声で言いました。「水からあがろう。そしたらぼくの身の上話を聞かせてあげるよ。そうすれば、ぼくが犬もネコも好きになれない理由がわかるよ」

　たしかに、そろそろ退散する時間でした。池は、水にはまった鳥や動物たちでごったがえしていたのです。あひるやドードー鳥や、インコやワシの子もいたし、他にも変わった動物たちが何匹かいました。アリスを先頭にして、みんなぞろぞろとアリスのあとに続き、岸に向かって泳いでいきました。

Chapter III

A Caucus Race and a Long Story

They were certainly a strange-looking group that met on the river bank—the birds and the animals were all very, very wet and unhappy.

The first question of course was, how to get dry again: they had talked about this, and after a few minutes it seemed quite normal to Alice to find herself talking with them, as if she had known them all her life. Alice talked for a long time with the Lory. After a while, the Lory said that because he was older than Alice he must know more than her. Alice asked the Lory to tell her his age, but he would not, so there was nothing more they could talk about.

At last the Mouse (who seemed to be a very important person in the group) called out, "Sit down, all of you, and listen to me! *I'll* soon make you dry enough!"

■ caucus 図 党大会　■ of course もちろん　■ get dry 乾く　■ all one's life 生まれてから（このかた）　■ at last ついに、とうとう　■ call out 叫ぶ

第3章
党大会（デタラメ）競争と長いお話

　岸辺に集まったのは、見るからにヘンテコな連中でした。鳥たちや動物たちはみんなびしょびしょに濡れて機嫌が悪そうでした。
　さしあたっての問題は、どうやって早く、からだを乾かすかでした。みんなでがやがや相談していました。数分後、生まれたときから知っていたかのように、みんなの仲間に入って話すことが、アリスにはごくあたりまえに思えてきました。アリスは長いことインコと話しました。しばらくすると、インコは、自分はアリスよりも年上だから、アリスよりも物知りだと言いました。アリスはインコの年を尋ねましたが、インコは教えてくれません。それで、もう話題がつきてしまいました。
　とうとうネズミ（みんなから一目おかれているようでした）が叫びました。「みんな座ってぼくの話を聞いてくれ！　そしたらすぐに君たちのからだを乾かしてあげよう！」

They all sat down at once in a large square with the Mouse in the middle. Alice kept looking at the Mouse because she wanted to get dry as quickly as possible so that she didn't get a cold.

"Ahem!" said the Mouse importantly. "Are you all ready? Be quiet, everyone, if you please!" He then started to tell them a long story so that they would not think about being wet.

After a while he asked Alice how she was. "As wet as ever," said Alice: "it doesn't seem to make me dry at all." So one of the birds suggested that they stop talking and that they start having a Caucus race.

"What *is* a Caucus race?" said Alice; not that she really wanted to know.

"Why," said the Dodo, "the best way to explain it is to do it." (And because you might like to try having a Caucus race yourself one winter day I will tell you how the Dodo arranged it.)

First it marked out a race-course in a sort of square (it does not really matter what the course is like), and then they were all placed along the course, here and there. There was no "One, Two, Three, and Away!" but they began running when they liked, and they stopped when they liked. So it was not at all easy to know when someone had won the race.

■ at once すぐに　■ so that ～できるように　■ get a cold 風邪をひく　■ mark out （線を引いて場所を）区切る、境界を定める　■ not that けれども～というわけではない　■ sort of ～のようなもの　■ not matter どうでもいい、問題にならない

みんなすぐさまネズミを真ん中にして、大きな四角で囲んで座りました。アリスは風邪をひくのはいやだったので、すぐさま乾かしたいと思い、じっとネズミを見つめ続けました。

　「えへん！」と、ネズミはえらそうに言いました。「諸君、よろしいかな？　静粛にしてくれたまえ！」　そして、みんなずぶ濡れだってことを忘れるぐらい、長いお話を始めたのでした。

　しばらくしてからネズミは、アリスに気分はどうか尋ねました。「あいかわらずびしょ濡れよ」とアリスは答えました。「あなたのお話を聞いても、ぜんぜん乾いてこないみたいよ」　そこで一羽の鳥が口をはさみ、もう話をやめて、党大会競争を始めようと提案しました。

　「党大会競争って何？」と、アリスは聞きました。別に本気で知りたかったわけではなかったんですが。

　「なあに」とドードー鳥。「一番てっとり早い説明方法は、やってみることだな」（みなさんも冬の日に、党大会レースをやってみたいかもしれないでしょうから、ドードー鳥がどうやってレースをアレンジしたか教えてあげましょう）。

　まず最初に、レース用の四角いコースを地面に描きました（どんな形をしていても大丈夫です）。そしてみんなをコースのあちこちの位置につかせました。「よーい、どん！」もなく、みんな好きなときに走り出し、好きなときにやめたので、いつ誰が勝ったのか知るのは難しかったのです。

However, when they had been running for half an hour or so, and they were quite dry again, the Dodo suddenly called out, "The race is over!" and they all crowded round it and asked, "But who has won?"

The Dodo could not answer this question without thinking for a long time. He thought for several minutes with one finger on his head, while everyone else waited quietly. At last the Dodo said, "*Everybody* has won, and you must *all* have prizes."

"But who is to give the prizes?" they asked.

"Why, *she*, of course," said the Dodo, pointing to Alice with one finger; and so all of them crowded round her, calling out, "Prizes! Prizes!"

Alice did not know what to do. The only thing she could think of was to put her hand in her pocket, and pull out a box of sweets (luckily the saltwater of the pool had not got into them so they were still dry). She decided to give them to everyone as prizes. Luckily there was one for each person.

"But she must have a prize herself, you know," said the Mouse.

"Of course," the Dodo replied. "What else have you got in your pocket?" it asked, turning to Alice.

"Only this," said Alice sadly.

"Give it to me," said the Dodo.

Then they all crowded round her once more while the Dodo said, "Please accept this beautiful prize."

■ or so ～かそこらで ■ over 形 終わって ■ crowd round 取り囲む ■ why 間 もちろん ■ pull out 引き出す、取り出す ■ sweets 名 甘い菓子、キャンディー ■ what else 他になにか

でも、30分ぐらい走り続けてみんなすっかり乾いたころ、ドードー鳥が突然叫びました。「競争やめーっ！」 みんなドードー鳥のまわりに集まってきて、聞きました。「それで、だれが勝ったの？」

この質問には、ドードー鳥はながいこと考えないと答えられませんでした。一本の指を頭に置いて数分考えました。その間、みんな静かに待っていました。とうとう、ドードー鳥は答えました。「みんなが勝ったのです。だからみんな賞品をもらわなくてはいけない」

「でも、いったいだれが賞品をくれるの？」みんなが尋ねました。

「そりゃ、あの子ですとも、もちろん」と、ドードー鳥は一本指でアリスを差して言いました。そこでみんな、「賞品！　賞品！」とわめきながら、アリスのまわりに群がってきました。

アリスはどうしていいのかわかりませんでした。ひとつだけ思いついたことは、ポケットに手を入れてお菓子の箱を取り出すことでした（幸い、池の塩水はお菓子の箱の中にしみ込んでいなかったので、お菓子は乾燥していました）。アリスは、お菓子をみんなに賞品として配ろうと思いました。ラッキーなことに、一人一個ずつ配れるだけのお菓子が箱には入っていました。

「でも、当然、この子も賞品をもらわなくはいけない」と、ネズミが言いました。

「もちろん」と、ドードー鳥が答えました。「ポケットの中には他に何が入っているのかい？」と、アリスをふり向いて聞きました。

「これだけよ」と、悲しそうにアリスは答えました。

「こっちによこしなさい」と、ドードー鳥。

するとみんな、もう一度アリスを取り囲みました。ドードー鳥は言いました。「この優雅な賞品をお納めください」

When he had finished this short speech they all cheered. Alice thought the whole thing was very strange, because the prize the Dodo had given her was something that was already hers—but they all seemed to think it was very important, so she did not want to laugh; and, as she could not think of anything to say, she just bowed and thanked them.

The next thing to do was to eat the sweets: This caused some noise and problems as the large birds said that there was no taste in their sweets, and the small ones found it difficult to eat theirs. However, finally they finished, and then they sat down again and asked the Mouse to tell them another story.

"You promised to tell me the story of your life, you know," said Alice, "and why it is that you hate—C's and D's," she added very quietly. "My story is long and sad!" said the Mouse turning to Alice.

The Mouse started to tell his story, but he soon stopped and walked away because he didn't think anyone was listening.

"Please come back and finish your story!" cried Alice. And all the others cried, "Yes, please do!" But the Mouse only shook its head and walked a little quicker.

"I wish Dinah was here," said Alice. "She'd soon get the Mouse back!"

"And who is Dinah?" asked the Lory.

■ cheer 動 歓声をあげる　■ bow 動 お辞儀をする　■ cause 動 〜を引き起こす
■ taste 名 味　■ walk away 立ち去る　■ shake one's head 首を横に振る

短いスピーチを終えると、みんな歓声をあげました。アリスには、なにからなにまで、すべてがデタラメに思えました。だって、ドードー鳥から授けられた賞品は、もともとアリスのものだったからです。でもみんなにとってはとても重要な儀式に思えたので、アリスは笑いをこらえました。何も言うことが思いつかなかったので、お辞儀をして、みんなに感謝しました。

次にやるべきことは、お菓子を食べることでした。大きな鳥たちはお菓子に味がないと文句を言い、小さな鳥たちは、飲み込むのに苦労したり、さわぎと問題が起こりました。ようやくみんな無事に食べ終えると、もう一度座って、ネズミに別のお話をしてくれとせがみました。

「あなたの生い立ちを話してくれるって言ったでしょう」と、アリスは言い、「それを聞いたら、なぜあなたがネーとか、イーとかが嫌いなのかわかるって」と、そっとつけたしました。「ぼくの物語はとても長くて悲しいんだ」とネズミはアリスに向かって言いました。
　ネズミは身の上話を始めました。でも、だれも聞いていないと思い、すぐに話をやめて立ち去ってしまいました。
　「お願いだからもどってきて、お話を続けてちょうだい！」と、アリスは叫びました。ほかのみんなも一緒に、「お願いします！」でも、ネズミは頭を横に振って、足を速めて行ってしまいました。
　「ダイナちゃんがここにいてくれたらなあ」と、アリスは言いました。「ダイナなら、すぐにネズミを連れもどしてくれるのに！」
　「ダイナっていったいだれ？」と、インコが尋ねました。

Alice replied happily, because she was always ready to talk about her cat: "Dinah's our cat. And she's a very good cat for catching mice! I wish you could see her running after the birds! She eats a bird as soon as she looks at it!"

This speech caused a big reaction in the group. The birds started to hurry away making excuses that it was time to go home and that their children should be in bed. Soon Alice was left alone.

"I wish I hadn't said anything about Dinah!" she said to herself. "Nobody seems to like her down here, and I'm sure she's the best cat in the world! Oh, my dear Dinah! I wonder if I shall ever see you again!" And then poor Alice began to cry again, for she felt very lonely and unhappy. Soon, however, she heard someone walking in the distance so she looked up, hoping that the Mouse had decided to come back and finish his story.

■ ready to いつでも〜できる ■ run after 〜を追いかける ■ reaction 名 反応 ■ make excuses 弁解する、言い訳する ■ be left alone 独りぼっちになる ■ down here ここには ■ look up 見上げる

アリスはうれしそうに答えました。いつも自分の猫のことを話すのは大好きだったからです。「ダイナちゃんはね、わたしのうちのネコなの。ネズミを捕まえるのがすごく上手なのよ。それに鳥たちを追いかけるところを見せてあげたいわ。鳥を見つけたとたん、ひと飲みにするのよ！」

　アリスの発言は大きな動揺を生みました。鳥たちは、早く家に帰って子どもたちを寝かせつけなきゃとか言いわけをして、あたふたと立ち去っていきます。やがてアリスは、また一人ぼっちになってしまいました。

　「ダイナちゃんのことを話さなければよかった！」と、つぶやきました。「ここではだれもダイナちゃんのことを好きな人はいないみたい。ぜったいに、世界一のネコなのに！　ああ、わたしの可愛いダイナ！　いつかまた、あなたと会えるのかしら！」　そう言うと、かわいそうに、アリスはまた泣き出してしまいました。とっても心細くなって、がっくりきてしまったのです。すぐに、遠くから足音が聞こえてきました。アリスははっと顔を上げました。もしかしたら、ネズミがもどってきて、身の上話の続きをしてくれるかもしれないと期待したのでした。

Chapter IV

The Rabbit Needs Little Bill's Help

It was the White Rabbit walking slowly back again and looking as if it had lost something. She heard it saying to itself, "The Duchess! The Duchess! She will kill me! Where *can* I have dropped them, I wonder!" Alice guessed in a moment that the Rabbit was looking for the fan and the pair of white gloves, so she very kindly began looking about for them, but they were nowhere to be seen—everything seemed to have changed since her swim in the pool, and the great hall, with the glass table and the little door, had disappeared completely.

Very soon, the Rabbit noticed Alice and called out to her in an angry voice, "Mary Ann, what *are* you doing out here? Run home this moment, and fetch me a pair of gloves and a fan! Quick now!" And Alice was so afraid that she ran off at once in the direction it pointed to, without trying to explain that she was not Mary Ann.

■ lost 動 lose（なくす）の過去分詞形　■ kindly 副 親切に　■ look about for ～を捜し回る　■ nowhere to be seen 影も形もない　■ out here こんなところで　■ fetch 動 ～行って取ってくる　■ run off 逃げ去る

第 4 章
ウサギのお使い、小さなビル

　もどってきたのは、またあの白ウサギでした。どうやら何か探し物をしている様子で、ゆっくりと歩いてきます。アリスの耳に入ってきたのは、「公爵夫人が！ 公爵夫人が！ このままじゃ、処刑されてしまう！ いったいぜんたい、どこに落としてしまったんだろう！」 アリスにはすぐにわかりました。ウサギが探しているのは、扇子と白手袋だってことが。それで、アリスは、親切にまわりを見わたして探してあげました。でも、どこにも見当たりません。涙の池を泳いだあとは、なにもかも変化してしまったようです。大広間も、ガラスのテーブルも、小さな扉も、ぜーんぶ、完全に消えてしまっていました。
　すぐにウサギはアリスに気づき、怒った口調でどなりつけました。「メアリー・アン、お前はここで何してるんだ？　今すぐ家にもどって、手袋と扇子を取ってきなさい！　さあ早く！」 怖気づいたアリスは、ウサギが指さした方向に向かって、一目散に駆けだしました。自分がメアリー・アンではないことを説明する余裕もなかったのです。

"He thinks I am his servant Mary Ann," she said to herself as she ran. "How surprised he'll be when he finds out who I am! But I should take his fan and his gloves to him—if I can find them." As she said this, she came to a little house, on the door of which she could see the name "W. RABBIT." She went in and hurried upstairs. She was very worried that she might meet the real Mary Ann, and then she would be told to leave the house before she had found the fan or the gloves.

"How strange it seems," Alice said to herself, "to be doing things for a rabbit! I suppose Dinah'll be asking me to do things soon!" And she began thinking about the sort of thing that would happen: Alice's nurse would say "Miss Alice! Come here now and get ready for your walk." Alice would then say "Coming in a minute—I've got to watch this mousehole for Dinah until she comes back. Dinah has told me to watch it so that the mouse doesn't escape." But Alice realised that they would probably not let Dinah stay in the house if she (a cat) began ordering people about like that.

By this time she had found her way into a nice little room with a table by the window, and on it (as she had hoped) she saw a fan and two or three pairs of tiny white gloves: She picked up the fan and one of the pairs of gloves and was just going to leave the room when she saw a little bottle. The last bottle she had seen had had the words "DRINK ME" on it but this one had nothing. However, she decided to drink it because she was sure *something* interesting would

■ servant 名 召使　■ go in 〜に入る　■ upstairs 副 上の階に　■ suppose 動 〜と想像する　■ nurse 名 乳母　■ get ready 支度をする　■ have got to 〜しなければならない　■ mousehole 名 ネズミの穴　■ find one's way やっとたどり着く

Chapter IV

「ウサギはわたしのことを召使のメアリー・アンと間違えちゃったんだわ」と、ぶつぶつ言いながら走りました。「わたしがほんとうは誰だかわかったら、さぞかし驚くでしょうね！ でも、もし扇子と手袋が見つかったら、ウサギにわたしてあげましょう――どこにあるのかわかればの話だけどね」 そう言いながら、アリスは、『白・ウサギ』と扉に名前が書かれた小さな家にたどり着きました。中に入って、急いで階段をかけ上がりました。うっかり本物のメアリー・アンに出くわして、扇子と手袋を見つける前に、出て行くように言われてしまったらどうしようと、内心、すごくびくびくしていました。

「わたし、すごくおかしなことをしているみたいに思われるわ」と、アリスはひとりごとを言いました。「ウサギの使い走りをしているなんて！ この調子じゃ、今度はきっとダイナの番で、わたしにあれこれ指図してくるに違いないわ！」 次に、これから起こりうるさまざまなことを想像してみました。アリスの婆やはきっとこう言うでしょう。「アリスお嬢さま！ 散歩のお時間ですから、今すぐいらしてくださいな」 するとアリスは答えるでしょう。「すぐに行くわ。でもダイナがもどってくるまで、このネズミ穴を見張っていなくてはならないの。ダイナから、ネズミが逃げないようにちゃんと見張っているように言われているから」 でも待って、アリスはすぐに気づきました。人間に命令するようになったダイナは、きっと家には置いてもらえなくなるだろうってことに。

そうこうしているうちに、アリスは窓辺にテーブルが置かれた素敵な小さなお部屋に入りこんでいました。そしてテーブルの上には、期待どおり、扇子と、2、3組の白手袋が置かれていたのです。扇子と一組の手袋を取って部屋を出ようとしたとき、小さなビンがアリスの目に飛び込んできました。最後に見たビンには、『アタシヲノンデ』と書かれたメモが結びつけられていましたが、このビンには何もついていません。でも、きっとまた、何かおもしろいことが

happen. So many interesting things had happened to her because of things she had drunk or eaten, so she wanted to discover what would happen if she drank this bottle.

"I do hope it'll make me grow large again, because I don't want to be such a small little girl anymore!"

It did! And much sooner than she had expected: Before she had drunk half the bottle, she found her head pressing against the top of the room, and she had to move it down so that her neck would not be broken. She quickly put down the bottle, saying to herself "That's quite enough—I hope I shan't grow any more. I can't get out of this room. I do wish I hadn't drunk quite so much!"

But it was too late to wish that! She went on growing and growing, and very soon she had to lie down with one arm against the door and the other arm out of the window and one foot up the chimney. She said to herself, "Now I can't move any more. What *will* happen to me?"

Luckily for Alice, she had stopped growing, but it was very difficult not being able to stand up, and, as there seemed to be no chance of her ever getting out of the room again, she felt very unhappy.

■ put down 下に置く　■ That's quite enough. もうこのくらいで十分。
■ shan't shall not（～すべきではない）の縮約形　■ get out of ～から外へ出る
■ chimney 图 煙突　■ no chance 見込みがない

起こるに違いないと期待して、ビンの中身を飲むことにしました。だって、アリスが飲んだり食べたりしたら、たくさんのおもしろいことが次々と起こったんですもの。だから、これを飲んだら、次に何が起こるのか試してみたかったのです。

　「また大きくなればいいのになあ。だって、こんなに小さな女の子のままでいるなんて、もううんざり！」

　すると、ほんとうにアリスの願い通りになりました。それも、思ったよりもずっと早く。ビンの半分を飲み干す前に、アリスの頭はお部屋の天井につっかえてしまい、首が折れないように、頭をひっこめました。すぐにアリスはビンを下に置いてつぶやきました。「もうこれで十分。これ以上背が伸びたら部屋から出られなくなってしまうわ。こんなにたくさん飲まなければよかった」

　でも残念ながら、もう手遅れでした。アリスの背はぐんぐんと伸び続けました。アリスは、床にはいつくばって、片腕をドアにくっつけ、もう片方の腕を窓から出し、片足は煙突の中に突っこまなくてはなりませんでした。そしてつぶやきました。「これじゃあ身動きできないわ。わたしこのまま、どうなるのかしら？」

　幸い、アリスの成長はそこで止まりました。とはいえ、起き上がることもできなくて、ほんとに大変でした。もうこの部屋から出られる見込みもなさそうだったので、アリスはすっかり落ち込んでしまいました。

"It was much nicer at home," thought poor Alice, "when I didn't always grow larger or smaller and I wasn't ordered around by mice and rabbits. I almost wish I hadn't gone down that rabbit-hole—but—this kind of life is rather interesting. I do wonder what has happened to me. Somebody should write a book about me. When I grow up I will write one!" Then she started to worry that she would not get any older and that she would never be able to learn any more or be an old woman because she could not leave the house that she was now in. She went on thinking these sad thoughts until, a few minutes later, she heard a voice outside, so she stopped to listen.

"Mary Ann! Mary Ann!" said the voice. "Bring me my gloves this minute!" Then came the sound of feet on stairs. Alice knew it was the Rabbit coming to look for her, and she started shaking till she shook the whole house.

She was so worried that she completely forgot that she was, in fact, now about a thousand times as large as the Rabbit, and so she had no reason to be afraid of it.

Soon the Rabbit came up to the door and tried to open it; but, as the door opened into the room, the Rabbit could not open the door, because Alice's arm was pressed against it. Alice heard the Rabbit say that it would go round and get in at the window.

■ be ordered around by ～にあれこれと指図される　■ get older 年を取る
■ outside 副 戸外で　■ this minute 今すぐ　■ stairs 名 階段　■ look for ～を探す
■ a thousand times 千倍　■ be afraid of ～を恐れる　■ get in ～の中に入る

Chapter IV

「こんなことならおうちにいればよかったわ」 かわいそうなアリスは思いました。「だって、おうちにいたときには、こんなにしょっちゅう、大きくなったり小さくなったりしなかったし、ネズミやウサギにあれこれ指図されることもなかったわ。ウサギの穴に飛びこまなかったらよかったのかもしれない。──とはいっても、今の状態はけっこうおもしろいわね。いったいわたしに何が起こったのかしら。わたしのお話を誰か本に書くべきよ。わたしが大きくなったら、ぜったいに本に書くわ！」 そして、アリスは不安になりました。もう年もとらないし、これ以上何も覚えることもできないし、おばあさんになることもない。だって、この家から一生出られないんですもの。悲しいことに思いをめぐらせて数分たったころ、家の外で声が聞こえました。心配するのはやめて、アリスはその声に耳を傾けました。

「メアリー・アン！　メアリー・アン！」と叫んでいます。「今すぐ、わたしの扇子と手袋を持ってきなさい！」 そして、階段を上る足音が聞こえました。白ウサギが彼女を探しにきたことがわかったので、アリスは体を震わせました。家はぐらぐらと揺れました。

不安だったので、今ではウサギの1000倍も大きくなったことを、アリスはすっかり忘れてしまっていました。だから、もうなにもこわくないことも。

ウサギは2階のドアを開けようとしましたが、ドアは内開きで、アリスの腕に押しつけられていたので、開きません。外にまわって窓から入るとウサギが言っているのが聞こえました。

"You can't come in this window," Alice decided, so, when she thought she heard the Rabbit just under the window, she quickly put her hand further out the window and moved it around. She did not feel anything, but she heard a little cry and a fall and then the sound of glass breaking. She decided that it was possible that the Rabbit had fallen into something made of glass.

Then she heard an angry voice—the Rabbit's—"Pat! Pat! Where are you?" And then a voice she had never heard before, "I'm here! I'm looking for apples, sir!"

"Looking for apples!" said the Rabbit angrily. "Here, come and help me get out of *this*!" Alice then heard more sounds of broken glass.

"Now tell me, Pat, what's that in the window?"

"It's an arm, sir!"

"An arm! Who has ever seen an arm as big as that one! It fills up the whole window!"

"It certainly does, sir: but it's definitely an arm."

"Well, why is it there—go and take it away!"

■ put out 外に出す　■ further 副 さらに遠く　■ move around あちこち移動させる　■ made of glass ガラスでできた　■ sir 名 旦那様《丁寧な呼びかけ》　■ definitely 副 間違いなく、疑いなく　■ take away 取り除く、撤去する

Chapter IV

「この窓からは入れないわよ」と、アリスは決めて、待ちかまえました。だから、ウサギが窓のすぐ下に来たような音が聞こえたとき、すぐに窓から腕をぐーんと伸ばして、ぐるぐるとまわしてみました。何も手に触れませんでしたが、小さな悲鳴と、何かが落ちる音に続いて、ガラスが割れる音が聞こえました。ウサギが何かガラスでできたものの中に落ちたのかもしれないと、アリスは思いました。

次に、どなり声が聞こえました。ウサギの声です。「おいパット、パット！　どこにいる？」　すると、初めて聞く声が聞こえてきました。「ここです！　リンゴを探しております。だんなさま！」

「なに、リンゴを探しているだと！」と、カンカンに怒ったウサギは言いました。「すぐにここにきて、わたしをここから出してくれ！」　またまたガラスが割れる音が聞こえてきました。

「なあ、パット。窓の中に見えるあれはいったい何だ？」

「腕でございます」

「腕だと！　あんなに巨大な腕を見たことがあるか！　窓いっぱいのデカさではないか！」

「そのとおりでございます。しかし、たしかに腕に違いありません」

「では、なぜあそこに腕があるのだ？　すぐに行って取っぱらってこい！」

There was a long silence after that and Alice could only hear a few sounds now and then, such as "I don't like it at all!" or "Do as I tell you!" and at last Alice put out her hand again and moved it around (as she had done before). This time there were two little cries and more sounds of glass breaking.

Alice then wondered what they would do next. She was very unhappy that they could not get her out of the room as she did not want to stay there any longer.

She waited for some time without hearing anything more: at last came the sound of some voices all talking together: she heard the words, "Where's the other ladder?" "Bill's got the other one." "Put them here." "No, tie them together first, because they don't reach up high enough." "Be careful of the roof of the house." "Now, who is going to go down the chimney—here, Bill—the Rabbit says you must go down the chimney!"

"Oh, so Bill's been told to come down the chimney, has he?" said Alice to herself. "Why does Bill have to do everything! I wouldn't like to be Bill: This chimney is very small." She pulled her foot back down the chimney a little bit and then waited till she heard a little animal (she couldn't guess what kind of animal it was) in the chimney above her. Then, saying to herself, "This is Bill," she gave one hard kick, and waited to see what would happen.

■ now and then ときどき ■ any longer これ以上 ■ for some time しばらくの間 ■ ladder 图 はしご ■ have got 持っている ■ to be 〜になる ■ wait to see 出方を見る、静観する

Chapter IV

　そのあと、長い沈黙が続きました。とぎれとぎれ聞こえてきたのは、「かんべんしてくださいよ！」や、「命令通りにしろ！」という言葉でした。アリスはとうとう、もういっぺん手を伸ばしてぐるぐるとまわしてみました（前にやったように）。今度は、小さな悲鳴が2人分聞こえて、さらにガラスの割れる音が響きました。

　さて、ウサギたちは次に何をするかしらと、アリスは考えました。誰もアリスをこの家から出してくれないので、とても悲しくなりました。だって、この状態でいるのはもう限界でしたから。

　なにも音が聞こえなくなりましたが、アリスはしばらく待つことにしました。やがて、いろんな声が重なりあって聞こえてきました。「もうひとつのはしごをどこへやった？」「ビルが持っております」「ここに二つとも持ってこい」「ダメだ。さきに、二つのはしごをつないで縛っておけ。そうしないと上まで届かないぞ」「屋根に気をつけろ」「さあと、煙突は誰に下りていかせようかなあ、そうだ、ビル、ウサギのだんながおまえに煙突に入れと言っているよ！」

　「あらまあ、それじゃあビルが煙突を下りていくように言われたのかしら？」とアリスはつぶやきました。「でもなぜビルがなにもかもやらなくてはいけないのかしら！　わたしだったらぜったいビルになりたくないわ。この煙突はとっても小さいんですもの」　アリスは煙突から足をちょっぴりひっこめて、待ちかまえました。そうしたら、小さな動物（何の動物か見当がつきませんでした）が、煙突の上の方で、ガサゴソやっているのが聞こえてきました。「きっとビルだわ」　アリスはつぶやきました。そして、思いっきりキックして、次に何が起こるのか待ちました。

The first thing she heard was everyone shouting "There goes Bill!" Then the Rabbit's voice alone"—Catch him!" Then silence, and then another sound of voices—"Hold up his head, give him some brandy. Now, don't give him too much. How was it, Bill? What happened to you? Tell us all about it!"

Finally, she heard a weak, little voice. ("That's Bill," thought Alice.) "Well I don't really know. That's enough brandy, thank you. I'm better now—but I can't tell you what happened. All I know is something kicked me and I flew back up the chimney."

"We saw that!" said the others.

"We must start a fire in the house!" said the Rabbit, and Alice called out as loud as she could, "If you do that, I'll get Dinah to come and eat you!"

There was complete silence, and Alice thought to herself, "I wonder what they *will* do next! If they had any good ideas they would take the roof off."

After a minute or two, they began moving about again, and Alice heard the Rabbit say, "We'll start with a few." Alice wondered, "A few of *what*?" But she did not have long to wait because in the next moment some small stones came flying in at the window, and some of them hit her in the face. "I'll stop this," she said to herself, and shouted out, "You'd better not do that again!" after which there was more silence.

■ there goes どこかへ行ってしまう　■ hold up 支える　■ brandy 图 ブランデー　■ start a fire 火を付ける　■ take ~ off ~を外す　■ move about 動きまわる　■ start with ~から始める　■ shout out 大声で叫ぶ　■ had better not ~しない方が良い

最初に聞こえてきたのは、みんながいっせいに叫ぶ声でした。「ビルが飛んでいくぞー！」次に、ウサギの声だけが聞こえました。「ビルをキャッチしろ！」そしてシーンとなったかと思ったら、たくさんの声が聞こえてきました。「頭を支えて、気つけのブランデーを飲ませろ。飲ませすぎるなよ。なあどうだった、ビル？　いったい何が起こったんだ？　ぜんぶ話してくれ！」

最後に、消え入りそうな声が聞こえてきました。(「きっとビルだわ」と、アリスは思いました。)「えーっと、自分でもよくわからないんです。もうブランデーは十分いただきました。ありがとうございます。おかげで気分が少しよくなりました。でも、何が起こったのかはお話しできません。ただ覚えているのは、何かに蹴飛ばされて、煙突から吹き飛んだってことです」

「見えたよ！」 みんなが言いました。

「この際、家を燃やすしかないな！」と、ウサギの声。すぐにアリスはあらん限りの大声を張り上げて叫びました。「そんなことをしたら、ダイナを連れてきて、みんな、ペロリと食べられちゃうからね！」

あたりは死んだように静まりかえりました。アリスは一人考えました。「次に何をしでかすのかしら！　みんなちょっとは知恵を働かせて、屋根を取りはずせばいいのに！」

1分か2分たったあと、またみんなは動き出しました。ウサギが、「それでは少しずつ始めよう」と言う声が聞こえました。「少しずつって、いったい何のことかしら？」と、アリスは思いました。次の瞬間、小石の雨がぱらぱらと窓から飛びこんできたので、答えを長く待つ必要はありませんでした。小石が何個かアリスの顔にあたりました。「やめさせてやるわ！」と、アリスはつぶやいて、どなりました。「すぐにおやめなさい！」 またもや、沈黙です。

Alice noticed, with some surprise, that the stones were all turning into little cakes as they lay on the floor, and she had a clever idea—"If I eat one of these cakes," she thought, "it must change my size; and, as it can't possibly make me larger, it must make me smaller." So she ate one of the cakes and was very happy to find that she began getting smaller. As soon as she was small enough to get through the door, she ran out of the house and found quite a lot of little animals and birds waiting outside. Bill was in the middle of the animals and he was being given something out of a bottle.

They all started running towards Alice as soon as they saw her, but she ran on as fast as she could and soon found herself safe in a thick wood.

"The first thing I've got to do," said Alice to herself, as she walked about in the wood, "is to grow to my usual size again; and the second thing is to find my way into that lovely garden. I think that is the best plan." It sounded like an excellent plan and it was very easily arranged; the only difficulty was that she had no idea how to do it; and, while she was looking about in the trees, a little sharp bark just above her head made her look up quickly.

■ turn into ～に変わる［変化する］　■ lay 動 lie（ある、置かれている）の過去形　■ clever 形 利口な　■ possibly 副《否定文で》とうてい～ない　■ run out of ～から駆け出して行く　■ quite a lot of 相当な数の　■ in a wood 森の中で　■ excellent 形 極めて良い　■ have no idea 全くわからない　■ bark 名（犬などの）ほえ声

驚いたことに、床に落ちた小石が次々とお菓子に変わっていくことにアリスは気づきました。とたんに、いい考えがひらめきました。「お菓子を一個食べたら、きっと体の大きさが変わるわ。もうこれ以上大きくなるはずがないので、きっと、ぜったいに小さくなるわ」　そこでアリスは、お菓子を一個食べました。すると、背が縮んでいくことがわかり、とてもハッピーでした。ドアを抜けることができるサイズになったとたん、アリスはいちもくさんに家を飛び出しました。外には、大勢の小さな動物や鳥たちがひしめいていました。その真ん中にビルがいました。ビンから何か飲ませてもらっていました。

　アリスの姿を見るやいなや、みんな一斉に、アリスに駆けよっていきました。でも、アリスは全速力で逃げたので、無事、深い森の中に身を隠すことができました。
　「さてと、まず最初にやるべきことは」と、アリスは森の中をさまよいながらつぶやきました。「いつものわたしの大きさにもどること。次にやるべきことは、あの素敵なお庭に行く方法をみつけること。これがベストプランだわ」アリスは素晴らしい計画を思いついたようでした。それに、簡単に準備できそうでした。ただし、どうやって実行したらよいのか、アリスにはまったくわからなかったことだけが、唯一の問題でした。森中をあちこち歩き回っていたら、小さな鋭い吠え声が頭の真上で響いたので、アリスはあわてて見上げました。

Alice's Adventures in Wonderland

A very big puppy (a baby dog) was looking down at her with large round eyes, and was trying to touch her. "Poor little thing!" said Alice, and she tried to make the puppy think she was a friend, but at the same time she was very, very afraid. She thought the puppy might be hungry and that it would want to eat her up because she was so small.

She didn't know what to do, but she picked up a stick of wood and showed it to the puppy: The puppy then jumped into the air and, with a cry of delight, rushed towards the stick. Then Alice ran behind some plants so that she could not be eaten by the puppy. As soon as Alice appeared on the other side of the plants, the puppy ran towards the stick again and fell over in its hurry to get to it. Then Alice, thinking that it was playing a game by itself, felt happier. But, because she thought it might still run over her, she ran round the plant again. The puppy went on playing—it ran a little way towards the stick and then a long way back, barking all the time. Finally it sat down with its mouth open, breathing very fast, and its big eyes half shut.

■ puppy 图 子犬　■ at the same time 同時に、そうは言っても　■ eat up 食べ尽くす　■ plant 图 植物、草　■ fall over 〜につまずいて転ぶ　■ in one's hurry to 〜しようと急いで　■ run over 〜の上を走る、〜を踏みつぶす　■ breathe 動 呼吸する

Chapter IV

　ものすごく大きな子犬（赤ちゃん犬）が、まんまるい大きな目でアリスを見下ろしています。そしてアリスに触れようとしています。「よしよし！」と言って、子犬にアリスはお友だちだと思ってもらおうとしました。でもほんとうは、ものすごく怖かったのです。子犬がお腹をすかせていて、小さなアリスを食べてしまったらどうしましょうと思ったからです。

　自分でも、どうしたらよいのかわかりませんでしたが、アリスは一本の小枝をひろい上げて、子犬に見せました。とたんに子犬は、うれしそうにワンと吠えて、空中に飛び上がり、小枝に飛びつきました。アリスは、急いで茂みの陰に隠れて、子犬に食べられないようにしました。アリスが茂みの反対側に移動した瞬間、子犬は再び小枝に向かって走り、小枝に飛びかかりました。それを見ていたアリスは、子犬が一人で遊んでいるんだと思い、ほっとしました。でも、もしかしたら子犬は、アリスに向かって飛びかかってくるかもしれないと思ったので、茂みの陰にふたたび身を隠しました。子犬は小枝とじゃれ続けました。小枝の少し前に走りこんでは、またずっとうしろに下がり、その間中、吠え続けていました。やがて座りこんで、口を開けて、はあはあ言いながら息をしています。大きな目は半分閉じてしまいました。

This seemed to Alice to be a good chance to run away: so she left at once and ran till she was quite tired and until she could not hear the puppy's bark anymore.

"But what a lovely puppy it was!" said Alice, as she rested after running such a long way. "I would like to have played with it, if—if only I'd been bigger! Oh dear, I'd nearly forgotten that I have to grow bigger again. Let me see, how can I grow again? I suppose I should eat or drink something; but the important question is 'What?'"

The big question certainly was "What?" Alice looked all around her at the flowers, the plants, and the grass, but she could not see anything that looked like the right thing to eat or drink. There was a large mushroom growing near her, about the same height as herself; and, when she had looked under it and on both sides of it and behind it, she realised that she should look and see what was on the top of it.

She stood up as high as she could and looked over the edge of the mushroom and saw a large blue Caterpillar sitting on the top of it with its arms crossed in front of it quietly smoking a long cigarette and not looking at her or anything else.

■ run away 逃げ出す　■ rest 動 休む　■ look like 〜のように見える　■ right thing 正しいこと　■ mushroom 名 キノコ　■ height 名 高さ、身長　■ look over 〜越しに見る　■ caterpillar 名 いも虫　■ with one's arms crossed 腕組みをして

Chapter IV

　逃げるなら今しかないと思い、アリスはすぐに走りだしました。くたくたになるまで、子犬の声が聞こえなくなるまで、ひたすら走り続けました。

「それにしても、かわいい子犬だったわ！」と、長いこと走り続けたあと、一休みしながらつぶやきました。「いっしょに遊びたかったわ。もうちょっとわたしが大きかったらね！　まあいけない、また大きくならなくちゃいけないことを忘れるところだったわ。さあてと、どうやったらまた背が伸びるかしら。たぶん、何かを食べたり飲んだりしなくてはいけないと思うけど。でも、問題は、いったい"何"を？」

　たしかに、大問題は、「何を？」でした。アリスはあたりを見わたしました。花や植物や、草が生えていましたが、どれも、食べたり飲んだりするのにふさわしいものには見えませんでした。アリスのそばには、大きなキノコが生えていました。アリスの背丈と同じぐらいです。アリスはキノコの下をのぞいて、両側と、うしろ側を点検したあとに、気づきました。キノコの上に何があるのか、確かめなくてはならないことを。

　アリスはつま先立ちになってうんと背のびしました。そして、キノコのかさのへりごしに上を見わたすと、大きな青いイモムシが、てっぺんに座っているのが見えました。腕組みをして、長いキセルを静かにくゆらせています。イモムシは、アリスも、ほかの何も、見ていませんでした。

覚えておきたい英語表現

> **what is the use of a book 〜** （p.8, 4行目）
> 本として役立つのかしら

【解説】the use of 〜 は、「（〜の）使用・使い道」という意味です。useful（役立つ）という形容詞は、頻繁に使われます。

【例文】① What is the use of living without you?
　　　　　君なしの人生なんて無意味だ。

　　　　② The meaning of life can be found in being useful.
　　　　　生きることの意味は、自分が役立つことによって見出すことができる。

> **unusual** （p.8, 14行目）
> 珍しい

【解説】unusualは、usual（普通）の反対ですから、「普通じゃない」「ヘンだ」という意味になります。アリスは、不思議の国で出会った生きものたちや出来事のことを、unusual、strange（妙な）や、curious（珍しい）といった形容詞を頻繁に使って表現しています。「嫌な」や、「気持ちが悪い」といった表現を使わないところに、アリスの教養とやさしさがあふれています。日常会話でも、「ヘンだ！」と思ったときに使える便利な表現ですが、unusual の方が、strange よりもやわらかい印象を相手に与えます。何かをためした後に意見を求められたら、「ヘンだ！」とか、「気持ちが悪い」、「好みじゃない！」と思っても、これらの表現を使えば、相手に不快感を与えません。different（違う・ユニーク・個性的）も、便利な表現ですので覚えておきましょう。

【例文】① It is indeed an unusual outfit.
　　　　　なるほど変わった（個性的な）よそおいだね。

　　　　② It tastes different, and a bit strange…
　　　　　ちょっと変わった、ユニークな味だわ。

♥ 1 ♥

> "Yes, that's about the right distance." （p.12, 10行目）
> 「正解。だいたいそれぐらいの距離ですね」

【解説】ものごとの right or wrong（可否）を常に問い続ける欧米諸国では、right（正しい）という単語は、日常茶飯事に使われています。

【例文】① Only YOU can find the right answer.
　　　　君だけが、正解を知っている。

　　　＊YOUにアクセントを置いてゆっくりと発音します。YOUのあとに少し間をおいて、文章を続けましょう。一方、rightにアクセントを置いて発音すると、「正解」を強調します。

　　② A: I believe in you.　　君を信じている。
　　　 B: Right!　　　　　　わかった！（そうよね！）

　　　＊Rightは、相づちを打つときに英国人が好んで使う単語です。「了解！」や「君の言うとおり」の意味もあります。説得力を持たせるためには、力強く、ゆっくりと、相手の目を見て語りかけましょう。

> "Dinah will miss me very much tonight." （p.12, 19行目）
> 「ダイナは今夜、わたしがいなくてすっごく寂しがるわ」

【解説】miss 〜 には、「〜がいないのを寂しく思う」や「〜の不在に気づく」、「〜に乗り損ねる」などの意味があります。

【例文】① I missed you!
　　　　寂しかったわ！

　　　＊大切な人と再会したときや、何かのイベントに欠席した人と会ったときに使える、シンプルで思いやりを込めた表現です。

　　② He's missing again! He must have missed the train again.
　　　　また彼がいない！また電車に乗り遅れたに違いないわ。

覚えておきたい英語表現

> **just in time to hear it say ～**（p.14, 5行目）
> ～と言っているのがちょうど聞こえました。

【解説】just in time は、「ぴったり間に合う」ことです。一方、Just-in-time は、ジャストインタイム・かんばん方式（トヨタ自動車が始めた生産管理方式で、在庫ゼロを目指して生産コストを下げるシステム）の意味もあります。

【例文】① He made it to the meeting just in time.
　　　　　彼は、会議にぎりぎり間に合った。

　　　　② I was just in time to see my best friend off at the airport.
　　　　　親友を空港で見送るのになんとか間にあった。

> **She found it very nice.**（p.18, 2行目）
> そしたらとても美味しかったのです。

【解説】ここでは、found（見つけた）の動詞を使って、それ以降の文章に対する発見や感想を述べています。つまり、ビンの中身を飲んだら、「（意外や意外）nice だった！」という意味です。

【例文】① I find you very attractive.
　　　　　あなたはとても魅力的だと思うわ。
　　　　　＊自分の目に相手がどう映っているのかを述べています。

　　　　② To my pleasant surprise, my mother
　　　　　found it delicious after her first try.
　　　　　母は、初めて試食してとても気に入ってくれたので、
　　　　　びっくりしたけどうれしかったわ。

　　　　　＊surprise（驚き）には、うれしいものとうれしくない
　　　　　　ものがあります。pleasant（楽しい）を前につけると、
　　　　　　「素敵なサプライズ」という意味になります。

♥ 1 ♥

> We won't talk about her any more, if you'd rather not.
> （p.32, 8行目）
>
> 彼女（ダイナちゃん）のことを話すのはもうやめましょう。話さない方がいいでしょう。

【解説】rather not は、「むしろ〜しない方がいい」と言う意味で、if you'd rather not talk about herを省略しています。

【例文】① I'd rather not mention his name.
　　　　あの人の名前はあえて口に出したくありません。

　　　② Would you rather have coffee than tea, Madam?
　　　　奥様は紅茶よりもコーヒーをお好みでしょうか？
　　　　＊英国的で非常に上品な表現です。

> "It certainly does, sir: but it's definitely an arm." （p.54, 17行目）
>
> 「そのとおりでございます。しかし、たしかに腕に違いありません」

【解説】certainlyもdefinitelyも、「たしかに」「もちろん」という意味で頻繁に使われる副詞です。強調したい箇所は、これらの副詞にアクセントを置き、ゆっくりと相手の目を見つめて発音すると、効果抜群です。

【例文】① I certainly agree with you.　　　　まったく同感です。

　　　② A: You're making a lot of sense.　　まったく、おっしゃる通りです。
　　　　B: Definitely!　　　　　　　　　　その通り！

　相手の意見に同意するときには、Yes（はい）の代わりに、Definitely! Certainly! Absolutely! などを使えば、一言で効果的に相手と"つながる"ことができます。あなたもぜひトライしてみましょう。
　まったく同意できないときには、notをつけ、Definitely not!（絶対に、反対です!）となります。not を強調して発音しましょう。

Free Space

Part 2

Chapter V-VIII

Chapter V
Help From a Caterpillar *p. 72*
イモムシが教えてくれたこと

Chapter VI
Pig and Pepper *p. 92*
ブタとコショウ

Chapter VII
A Mad Tea-Party *p. 112*
クレイジーお茶会

Chapter VIII
The Queen's Croquet Ground *p. 130*
女王陛下のクロッケー競技場

Chapter V

Help From a Caterpillar

The Caterpillar and Alice looked at each other for some time in silence: at last the Caterpillar took the cigarette out of its mouth and spoke to her in a sleepy voice.

"Who are *you*?" asked the Caterpillar.

This was not a good start for a conversation. Alice replied rather quietly, "I—I don't really know at the moment—I know who I was when I got up this morning, but I think I must have been changed several times since then."

"What do you mean by that?" asked the Caterpillar. "Tell me what you mean!"

"I'm very sorry but I can't tell you," said Alice, "because I'm not myself."

"I don't understand," said the Caterpillar.

■ each other お互いに　■ in silence 黙って、無言で　■ at the moment 今のところ
■ since then それ以来

第 5 章
イモムシが教えてくれたこと

　イモムシとアリスはしばらく黙ってお互いを見つめ合っていました。とうとう、イモムシは長いキセルを口から離して、眠そうな声でアリスに言いました。
「君はいったい何ものだね？」
　会話の始め方としてはあまりよいものではありませんでした。アリスはゆっくりと答えました。「わたし、あのー、実はわたしにもよくわからないんです。今朝目覚めた時の自分が誰だったかはわかるんですが、そのあとは何度も変化してしまったので」
「どういう意味だね？」と、イモムシは尋ねました。「説明してくれないか！」

「ごめんなさい。説明できないんです。だって、わたしはわたしじゃなくなってしまっているので」
「わからないなあ」と、イモムシ。

"I'm afraid I cannot explain it any more clearly," Alice replied very politely, "because I can't understand it myself, and being so many different sizes in one day is very strange."

"It isn't," said the Caterpillar.

"Well, perhaps you don't think so at the moment," said Alice, "but when you grow up you will, you know."

"No, I won't," said the Caterpillar.

"Well, perhaps *your* feelings may be different," said Alice: "all I know is, it feels very strange to *me*."

This brought them back again to the beginning of the conversation. Alice felt a little angry with what the Caterpillar had said, so she said very strongly, "I think you should tell me who *you* are first."

"Why?" asked the Caterpillar.

Here was another strange question; and as Alice could not think of any good reason, and the Caterpillar seemed to be *very* unkind, she turned away.

"Come back!" the Caterpillar called after her. "I've something important to say!"

This sounded good so Alice turned and came back again.

"Don't get angry," said the Caterpillar.

"Is that all?" said Alice trying to hide her anger.

"No," said the Caterpillar.

■ bring back （もとの場所に）戻す　■ Here is これは〜です　■ unkind 形 不親切な
■ turn away 背を向ける　■ call after 後ろから呼び掛ける　■ hide 動 隠す

「ごめんなさい、これ以上わかりやすく説明ができません」と、アリスはていねいに答え、「自分でもよくわからないからです。一日に何回も体の大きさが変わってしまうなんて、とても不思議なことなんですもの」

「そうかなあ」と、イモムシ。

「今はわからないかもしれませんが、あなたも成長したら、きっとわかるでしょう」と、アリス。

「いや、それは間違っている」と、イモムシ。

「もしかしたらあなたの感じ方はわたしとは違うかもしれませんね。でも、わたしにとって、とっても不思議に思えるんです」と、アリス。

そこで二人の会話はふりだしにもどりました。アリスは、イモムシが言ったことに少し腹をたてていました。そこで、口調を強めて言いました。「あなたが何者なのか、先に言うべきだと思います」

「なぜだい？」と、イモムシは聞きました。

またもや思いがけない質問をされてしまい、アリスには答えが見つかりませんでした。それに、イモムシはすごく不親切に思えたので、アリスはくるりと背を向けてしまいました。

「もどっておいで！」と、イモムシはアリスに向かって声をかけ、「大切なことを教えてあげるよ！」と、言いました。

それはぜひ聞きたいと思い、アリスはまたイモムシのところにもどってきました。

「怒らないで聞きなさい」と、イモムシは言いました。

「えっ、それだけ？」と、アリスは怒りをこらえて言いました。

「いや」と、イモムシ。

Alice thought she would wait, as she had nothing else to do, and she thought it might tell her something that would be good to hear. For some minutes it smoked and didn't speak; but at last it opened its arms, took the cigarette out of its mouth and said, "So you think you've changed, do you?"

"I'm afraid I have, sir," said Alice. "I can't remember anything now, and I don't stay the same size for longer than ten minutes!"

"*What* can't you remember?" asked the caterpillar.

"Well, I've tried to remember some things I learned at school, but I can't," replied Alice in a very sad voice.

"Repeat the poem *You're old, Father William* for me," said the Caterpillar.

Alice put her arms in front of her and began:—

"You are old, Father William," the young man said,
    "And your hair has become very white;
But you always stand on your head—
    Do you think at your age, it is right?"
"When I was young," Father William said to his son,
    "I was afraid it might be bad for my brain;
But now that I am sure I don't have one
    I do it again and again and again."

■ have nothing else to do 他に何もすることがない ■ be good to hear 良い知らせだ ■ put ~ in front of ~を(人)の前に置く ■ stand on one's head 逆立ちをする

Chapter V

　どうせほかに何もすることがなかったので、アリスはがまんして待つことにしました。もしかしたら、イモムシはアリスにとって得になることを言ってくれるかもしれないと期待したのです。イモムシはしばらくの間、黙ってキセルをぷかぷかとくゆらせていました。でもとうとう、組んでいた腕をほどいて、キセルから口を離すと言いました。「で、君は自分が変わってしまったと思っているんだね？」

「はい。残念ですが、おじさま、わたし、変わってしまったと思うんです」と、アリスは言いました。「今は何も思い出せないのですが、10分も同じ大きさでいられなくなってしまったのです！」

「思い出せないって、何を、だね？」と、イモムシは尋ねました。

「学校で習ったことを思い出そうとしても、ダメなんです」と、アリスは沈んだ声で言いました。

「じゃあ、『ウィリアム父さん、僕にとって父さんは年をとった』の詩を繰り返してみなさい」と、イモムシは言いました。

　アリスは、腕組みして詩の暗唱を始めました。

　　「もう年だよ、ウィリアム父さん」と、若い息子が言ったとさ。
　　　　「髪の毛だって真っ白。
　　なのに父さん、いつも逆立ちしてる。
　　　　そんなことしていいと思ってるの、その年で？」
　　「わしが若かったころは」ウィリアムは息子に言ったとさ。
　　「逆立ちしたら、オツムによくないと思ってた。
　　　　けれど今では、脳みそなんかすっからかん。
　　　　だから何度も何度も逆立ちするのさ」

77

"You are old," said the young boy, "as I said before,
　　And you have grown very fat;
But you jumped over backwards at the door
　　Tell me, why did you do that?"

"When I was young," said the old man,
　　"I kept my legs very fit
By using a cream from this can
　　So allow me to sell you a bit."

"You are old," said the young boy,
　　"and your mouth is too weak
　　For anything hard to eat;
But you ate all the bird's bones
　　and its beak
　　Tell me—how did you do it?"

"When I was young," said his father, "I studied law,
　　And talked about it with my wife
The strength it gave to my jaw
　　Has stayed with me all of my life."

■ grow fat 太る　■ jump over 飛び越える　■ backwards 副 後方へ[に・から]、逆さに
■ keep fit 健康を保つ、体調を整える　■ can 名 缶　■ allow 動 許す、許可する
■ beak 名 くちばし　■ law 名 法律　■ jaw 名 あご

「もういっぺん言うけど、父さんもう年だよ」若い息子は言ったとさ。
　　「おまけに、ずいぶん太ったよ。
なのにドアからバック転。
　　教えておくれ。なんでそんなことをするんだい？」

「わしが若かったころは」老人は言ったとさ。
　　「両足はしなやかそのもの。
このカン入り軟膏のおかげさ。
　　おまえも買わないか？」

「父さん年だよ」若い息子は言ったとさ。
　　「顎もがくがく。
　　固いものなんか食べられないよ。
なのに父さん、鶏の骨もくちばしも、
　　みんなぺろりとたいらげた。
　　なんでそんなことできるんだい？」

「若いころはな」父親は言ったとさ。「法律を勉強して、
　　母さんとがんがん弁論。
おかげで顎はがっちり鍛えられ、
　　今でも頑丈そのものさ」

"You are old," said the young boy, "so you would not think
     That you can see as well as ever;
But you could keep something on the end of your nose
     So tell me what made you so
     very clever?"

"I have answered three questions,
     and that is enough,"
     Said his father. "Don't be so self-centred!
Do you think I can listen to you all day?
     Go—or I will send you away from here!"

"That is not *quite* right," said the Caterpillar. "Not quite right—I'm sorry!" said Alice quietly; "Some of the words have been changed."

"It is wrong from the beginning to the end," said the Caterpillar in a very strong voice. And then there was silence for a few minutes.

The Caterpillar was the first to speak.

"What size do you want to be?" it asked Alice.

"Oh, I don't care what size I am," Alice replied quickly; "But I don't like changing so often."

"I *don't* understand why you don't like changing," said the Caterpillar.

■ as ever これまでのように ■ clever 形 上手な、器用な ■ self-centred 形 自己中心的な、身勝手な ■ send away 追っ払う ■ not quite right あまり正しくない ■ to be ～になる

「父さん年だよ」若者は言ったとさ。
　「視力も衰えただろう。
なのに鼻先になんかを乗っけることができる。
　なんでそんなに器用なの？」

「おまえの質問には3回答えた。
　だからもう十分」
　と、父親は言ったとさ。「わがままはもうおしまい！
お前の話に一日中つきあっていられると思うのか？
　もう行きなさい。さもなきゃ、おまえをここからつまみ出すぞ！」

「ちょっと違うなあ」と、イモムシは言いました。「ちょっと違うですって、ごめんなさい！」と、アリスは申しわけなさそうに言いました。「いくつか言葉が変わっちゃったみたい」
　「最初から最後まで、間違っておる」と、イモムシはきっぱり言いました。それから、しばらく沈黙が続きました。
　イモムシの方から先に口を開きました。
　「君はどれぐらいの大きさになりたいのかね？」と、アリスに尋ねました。
　「大きさなんてどうでもいいの」と、すぐさまアリスは答えました。「何度も何度も変わるのがいやなだけなんです」
　「なんで変化するのがいやなのか、わからないねえ」と、イモムシ。

Alice said nothing: She was feeling very angry again because the Caterpillar did not seem to understand her problem.

"Are you happy now?" said the Caterpillar.

"Well, I would like to be a *little* larger, Sir, if you wouldn't mind," said Alice: "three inches is very small."

"It is a very good height!" said the Caterpillar angrily, standing up as it spoke (it was three inches high).

"But it is very strange for me," said Alice, "because I am usually taller." And she thought to herself, "I wish the animals here would not get so unhappy so easily."

"You'll get used to it soon," said the Caterpillar; and it put its cigarette back into its mouth and began smoking again.

This time Alice waited patiently until it decided to speak again. In a minute or two the Caterpillar took the cigarette out of its mouth, breathed hard and then shook itself. Then it got down off the mushroom and went away into the grass saying, "One side will make you grow taller, and the other side will make you grow smaller."

"One side of what? The other side of what?" thought Alice to herself.

"Of the mushroom," said the Caterpillar, as if it had heard what she was thinking. In another moment she could not see the Caterpillar at all.

■ mind 動 嫌だと思う、気に障る　■ get used to ～に慣れる　■ patiently 副 辛抱強く
■ breath hard 荒い呼吸をする　■ shake oneself 身体を震わせる　■ get down off
～から下りる　■ in another moment 次の瞬間には

アリスは返事をしませんでした。もうかなり頭にきていたのです。だって、イモムシにはアリスの問題を理解できないようでしたから。
「今は満足してるかね？」と、イモムシ。
「そうね、もう少しだけ大きくなれたらいいなと思うけど、おじさま、もし言わせていただければ」と、アリス。「身長8センチにも満たないなんて、小さすぎると思うんです」
「それはとても立派な背丈だ！」と、イモムシは立ちあがって、むっとしたように言いました（イモムシの背丈も、8センチに満たなかったのです）。
「でもわたし、そんな背丈に慣れていないんです」と、アリスは言いました。「だっていつもはもっと大きいんですもの」 そしてつぶやきました。「ここの動物たちって、とても傷つきやすくて本当に困ったものだわ」
「すぐに慣れるよ」と、イモムシ。そしてキセルをまたくわえてぷかぷかとふかし始めました。
　今度は、アリスはしんぼう強く、イモムシが再び口を聞いてくれるのを待ちました。1、2分たつと、イモムシはキセルを口から離し、ぜいぜいと息をしたかと思うと、身ぶるいしました。それから、キノコから降りて、草の中にはって行きながら言いました。「片側なら大きくなるし、逆側なら小さくなる」
「何の片側？　何の逆側？」と、アリスは思いました。
「キノコだよ」と、イモムシ。まるでアリスの思いが聞こえたように答えました。次の瞬間、イモムシの姿はあとかたもなく消えていました。

Alice stood quietly looking at the mushroom for a minute, trying to decide which the two sides of it were; and, as it was completely round, she found this a very difficult problem. However, at last she put her arms round it as far as they would go, and broke two pieces off the mushroom with each hand.

"And now which is which?" she said to herself, and ate a little of the right-hand piece to see what would happen. The next moment she felt something hit her foot!

She was very frightened by this very sudden change, but she felt she must do something, as she was getting smaller and smaller very quickly. So she decided at once to eat some of the other piece. It was difficult for her to open her mouth, as it was so close to her foot, but she did it, and she ate some of the other bit of the mushroom. For a moment, she was very happy, but then she realised that she was growing so much that when she looked down all she could see was her neck. It seemed to be very, very long. She could not see her hands either. She started to move them about as she spoke but she still could not see them. They were too far away because her head and neck had now grown above the tops of the trees.

■ as far as 〜の所まで ■ break off もぎ取る
■ which is which どっちがどっちか ■ frightened 形 驚いた
■ bit 名 小片 ■ for a moment 一瞬 ■ far away 遠く離れて

Chapter V

　アリスは1分ほど、黙ってしげしげとキノコを見つめていました。いったいキノコのどちら側が片側で、どちら側が逆側なのかを見きわめようと努めたのです。でもキノコはまん丸でしたから、これはかなりの難題でした。ついにアリスは、キノコのまわりに両腕を思いっきりまきつけて伸ばし、両手でキノコの断片を2個もぎ取りました。

　「さて、どっちがどっちかしら？」　つぶやきながら、右手に持った切れはしを少しだけかじりました。次の瞬間、何かが足にぶつかるのを感じました！

　突然の変化に驚きましたが、またたく間に小さくなっていくので、すぐに何か手をうたねばと思いました。大急ぎでもうひとつの切れはしを食べようと思いましたが、口を開けるのさえ一苦労でした。口が足にくっつきそうだったからです。でもなんとか口を開いて、もう一つの切れはしにかじりつきました。一瞬ほっとしたのもつかの間、アリスの体はものすごく大きくなっていました。見下ろしてみると、自分の首しか見えません。ものすごく長い首になってしまったようです。自分の手も見えませんでした。声を出しながら手を動かしてみましたが、やはり見ることができません。アリスの手はずっとずっと遠くに行ってしまったのです。だって、アリスの頭と首が、木々を飛び越えるぐらいに伸びてしまっていたからです。

There seemed to be no chance of getting her hands up to her head, so she tried to get her head down to her hands, and she was very happy to find that her neck moved easily in any direction, like a serpent. She started to move her head down towards the tops of the trees, but stopped because suddenly a large pigeon (a kind of bird) flew into her face and started hitting her hard with its wings.

"Serpent!" cried the pigeon.

"I'm *not* a serpent!" said Alice angrily. "Leave me alone!"

"Serpent, I say again!" repeated the pigeon, but in a quieter voice. "I've tried every way but nothing seems right for them!"

"I really don't know what you are talking about," said Alice.

"I've tried everything," the pigeon continued, without listening to her; "but those serpents! You can never make them happy!"

Alice found it more and more difficult to understand what the pigeon was talking about, but she thought that she should not say anything more till the pigeon had finished speaking.

"It's very difficult making enough eggs," said the pigeon; "but I must also look out for serpents night and day! I haven't been able to sleep for at least three weeks!"

"I'm very sorry you've been upset," said Alice. She was beginning to understand what the pigeon was talking about.

"I had just found the tallest tree in the wood, so I thought I would be able to escape from serpents," continued the pigeon, "but then you came down from the sky! Serpents!"

■ serpent 图 ヘビ ■ pigeon 图 ハト ■ fly into 飛び込む ■ every way あらゆる点で ■ make someone happy （人）を喜ばせる ■ look out for 〜に注意［警戒］する ■ at least 少なくとも ■ upset 形 動揺して、腹を立てて

両手をいくら伸ばしてみても、頭に届きそうにありません。そこで、手に届くように、頭の方をぐんと下げてみました。すると、アリスの首はヘビのように、くねくねと、どの方向にも動いてくれることがわかり、ほっとしました。アリスは、空から頭をもたげて木立のてっぺんを見下ろそうとしましたが、すぐにやめました。突然、大きな一羽のハト（鳥の一種）がアリスの顔をめがけて飛んできて、翼でバタバタとアリスの顔を激しくぶち始めたからです。
　「このヘビめ！」と、ハトは金切り声をあげました。
　「ヘビじゃないわよ！」と、アリスは怒って言い返しました。「ほっといてよ！」
　「お前はヘビじゃないか。もう一度言うわよ！」と、ハトは繰り返しました。でも今度は少し落ち着いた口調です。「すべての手はうったのに、何ひとつうまくいかない！」
　「何のことかさっぱりわからないわ」と、アリス。
　「やるべきことはすべてやった」と、まるでアリスの言葉は耳に入らないかのようにハトは続けました。「ヘビのやつらは、執拗だ！」
　アリスには、ハトの言っていることがますますわからなくなりました。でも、ハトが話し終えるまで、口をはさむのはやめることにしました。
　「卵をかえすだけでも大変なのに」と、ハトが続けます。「でも、日夜ヘビが近づかないように見張っていなくてはならないのよ！　この3週間、一睡もしていないわ！」
　「大変だったのね、ほんとうにごめんなさい」と、アリスはあやまりました。やっと、ハトの話しが少しづつ理解できるようになってきました。
　「森の中で一番背の高い木を見つけたので、やっとヘビから解放されると思っていたのに」と、ハトは続けました。「なのに、こんどはあんたが空からくねくね降りてくるなんて！　ヘビめ！」

"But I'm *not* a serpent, I tell you!" said Alice. "I'm a…I'm a…"

"Well, *what* are you?" said the pigeon. "I can see you're trying to think of something!"

"I—I'm a little girl," said Alice, though she wasn't really certain. She remembered all the changes that had happened to her that day.

"I don't believe you!" said the pigeon. "I've seen many little girls in my life, but never *one* with such a long neck as you have! No, No! You're a serpent; there is nothing else you could be. I suppose you will now tell me that you have never eaten an egg!"

"I *have* eaten eggs, certainly," said Alice, who was a very truthful girl; "but little girls eat eggs as much as serpents do, you know."

"I don't believe it," said the pigeon; "but if they do, then they must be a kind of serpent; that's all I can say."

This was such a new idea to Alice that she was quite silent for a minute or two, which gave the pigeon the chance of adding, "You're looking for eggs, I know *that*; and what difference does it make to me if you are a girl or a serpent?"

"It makes a lot of difference to *me*," said Alice quickly; "but as it happens I am not looking for eggs and if I was I would not want *yours*: I don't like them uncooked."

■ think of something 何かを思いつく　■ truthful 形 正直な　■ as it happens たまたま、偶然にも　■ and if I was それにもし私がそうだとしても　■ uncooked 形 未調理の、生の

「でもわたしはヘビじゃないって言ってるでしょう！」と、アリス。「わたしは、わたしはね……」

「それであんたはいったい何なのよ？」と、ハト。「頭をひねっているようだね！」

「わたしは、わたしはね、小さな女の子よ！」と、アリスは言いました。ほんとうは、自信がなかったのですが。その日に自分に起きた変化を全部思い出していたのです。

「ウソつき！」と、ハト。「これまでずいぶん少女たちを見てきたけれど。あんたみたいに長い首をしたのは見たことがないわ！　ウソ、絶対にウソよ！ あんたはやっぱりヘビ。ヘビ以外にありようがないもの。どうせ次には、卵を食べたことがないなんて、言うつもりでしょう？」

「もちろん、卵は食べたことがあるわ」と、アリスは言いました。アリスはとても正直な女の子なのです。「だって、小さな女の子はみんな、ヘビ同様、卵を食べるんですもの。あなたにわかるかしら」

「そんなのウソ」と、ハト。「もし女の子も卵を食べるのなら、ヘビの仲間に違いない。それ以外ないわ」

まったく新しい発想に触れたアリスは、1、2分黙りこんでしまいました。それをいいことに、ハトが付け加えました。「あんたが卵を探してるってことはお見通しよ。だから、ヘビであろうと女の子であろうと、わたしにとって、同じことじゃない？」

「わたしには大違いよ」と、すかさずアリスは言い返しました。「おあいにくさま。わたしは卵なんか探していないし、もし探しているとしても、あなたの卵には興味がないわ。わたし、生玉子なんて、嫌いだもの」

"Well, go away, then!" said the pigeon as it started to feel safer. Alice tried to sit down but her neck was always getting caught in the trees. After a while she remembered that she was still holding some pieces of mushroom in her hands, and so she started very carefully eating first one bit and then the other—and so sometimes she grew taller and sometimes shorter, until she had reached her usual height.

It was such a long time since she had been near her usual size that it felt strange at first, but she quickly got used to it, so she began talking to herself as usual. She was much happier, but she still found all the changes very strange, as she never knew what size she was going to be. "However, half of my plan is complete, because I am now at my usual size—but the next thing I must do is get into that beautiful garden—how will I do that?" she said to herself. Just then, she suddenly came to an open place with a little house in it about four feet high. "Whoever lives there," thought Alice, "I can't visit them when I am *this* size; I would make them feel very afraid!" So she began eating some more of the piece from the right side of the mushroom and did not go near the house until she was nine inches high.

■ go away 立ち去る　■ get caught in 〜につかまって身動きがとれなくなる　■ talk to oneself ひとりごとを言う　■ as usual いつもの通り　■ open place 開けた場所　■ whoever 代 一体誰が《whoの強調》

「なら、とっといなくなってちょうだい！」 少しほっとしてハトは言いました。アリスは木々の間にしゃがもうとしましたが、首がどうしても枝にからまってしまい、うまくいきません。しばらくしてアリスは、手にキノコのかけらをまだ持っていることを思い出しました。そこで、注意深く、最初の切れはしをちょっとかじり、次の切れはしをちょこっとかじりました。身長はそのたびに伸びたり縮んだりしましたが、やがていつもの背丈にもどりました。

自分のいつもの身長にもどるのはほんとうに久しぶりで、最初は違和感を感じましたが、すぐに慣れました。そこでまた、お得意のひとりごとを始めました。アリスはすっかりいつもの陽気なアリスにもどっていました。でも、これまで起きた変化が不思議でたまりませんでした。だって、いつだって、不意に体の大きさが変化するのですから。「でも、わたしの計画の半分は達成したわ。だって、もとのサイズにもどったんですもの。さてっと、次にやるべきことは、あの素敵なお庭に出ること。でも、どうやって出たらいいのかしら？」と、アリスはつぶやきました。まさにその時、アリスは開けた場所に出ていました。そこには、1メートルちょっとの高さの小さな家が立っていました。「いったい、だれが住んでいるのかしら」と、アリスは考えました。「わたしの今のサイズだと、訪ねていったらびっくりされるから無理ね！」 そこで、アリスはまた、キノコの右側のかけらを食べ始めました。身長が20センチぐらいになってから、小さな家に近づいて行きました。

Chapter VI

Pig and Pepper

For a minute or two she stood looking at the house and decided what she should do next. Suddenly a footman came running out of the wood—(she thought he was a footman because of his clothes, but looking at his face she thought he was a fish). He knocked at the door of the house. It was opened by another footman with a round face and large eyes like a frog. He was also dressed like a footman. Alice wanted to know what was happening so she walked a little way out of the wood so that she could hear what they were saying.

The Fish-Footman began by giving the Frog-Footman a big letter, nearly as large as himself and said in a slow, important-sounding voice, "For the Duchess. The Queen is asking her if she would like to play croquet." The Frog-Footman repeated it in the same kind of voice—only changing the order of the words a little. "From the Queen. A letter asking the Duchess if she would like to play croquet."

Then they both bowed low.

■ pepper 名 コショウ　■ footman 名 従僕　■ knock 動 ノックする　■ way out of ～から抜け出る道　■ begin by ～から始める、まず～する　■ croquet クロッケー《芝生のコートで行われるイギリス発祥の球技》　■ order 名 順序

第 6 章

ブタとコショウ

　アリスは 1、2 分、その小さな家を見つめ、次に何をすべきか考えました。突然、森の中から従僕が走ってきました——（制服を着ていたので、アリスには従僕に見えたのでした。でも顔を見たらサカナのようでした）。サカナは小さな家のドアをノックしました。扉を開けたのは、もう一人の従僕でした。こちらは丸顔にカエルみたいなギョロ目をしていました。服装は従僕そのものでした。アリスは様子をさぐりたくなって、森から少し離れて二人の従僕の会話が聞こえるところまでそっと近づいていきました。

　まず最初に、サカナ従僕は、身の丈ほどもある大きな手紙をカエル従僕にわたしました。そして、低い、もったいぶった口調で言いました。「公爵夫人へ。女王陛下よりクロッケーのゲームへの御招待でござる」　カエル従僕も同じくもったいぶった口調でくりかえしました。でも少しだけ語順を変えて言いました。「女王陛下より。公爵夫人へ、クロッケーのゲームへの御招待でござる」

　そして二人は深々とお辞儀をしました。

Alice laughed so much at this that she ran back into the wood so that they would not hear her. When she next looked out, the Fish-Footman had gone and the other one was sitting on the ground.

Alice went quietly up to the door and knocked.

"I don't know why you are knocking," said the Frog-Footman, "for two reasons. First, because I'm on the same side of the door as you are: and secondly, they are making such a noise inside that no one could possibly hear you." And certainly there *was* a very loud noise coming from inside.

"Please tell me how I can get in?" said Alice.

"You could knock," the Frog-Footman replied (without really listening to her), "if we had the door between us. For example, if you were *inside*, you might knock, and I could let you out." He was looking up into the sky all the time he was speaking, and Alice thought this was very impolite.

"But perhaps he can't do anything else," she said to herself. "His eyes are so *very* near the top of his head. But he could answer my questions." Then she repeated "How can I get in?" as loud as she could.

"I will sit here," the Frog-Footman said, "till tomorrow…"

■ look out（中から）外を見る　■ for example 例えば　■ look up into ～を見上げる
■ impolite 形 失礼な

この光景を見て思わず笑いころげたアリスは、聞こえては大変と、急いで森の中へ駆けもどりました。次にのぞいてみると、サカナ従僕はいなくなっていました。もう一人は地べたに座りこんでいました。
　アリスはそーっと近づいて、ドアをノックしました。
「なぜドアをノックしてるのか、疑問だね」と、カエル従僕は言いました。「二つ理由がある。一つは、わしはあんたと同じく、ドアのこちら側にいる。二つ目の理由は、ドアの向こう側では大騒ぎの真っ最中。だれにもあんたのノックなんか聞こえやしないよ」　たしかに、家の中からすさまじい物音が聞こえてきました。
「どうやったら中に入れるのか教えていただけませんか？」と、アリスは尋ねました。
「ノックしてみたら」と、カエル従僕は答えました（アリスの言葉をちゃんと聞いていなかったのです）。「わしらの間に一枚の扉があったとする。そして、もしあんたが内側にいてノックしたら、わしはあんたを外に出してあげられる」　カエルはそうやって話している間も、ずっと空を見上げていました。それはとても失礼な行為だとアリスは思いました。
「もしかしたら、どうしようもないのかもしれないわ」と、アリスはつぶやきました。「だってカエル従僕の目は、頭のてっぺんについているんですもの。それでも、わたしの質問に答えることはできるはずだわ」　そこでアリスは、「どうやったら中に入れるんですか？」と、ありったけの声を振り絞って、もう一度尋ねました。
「わしはここに座っているとしよう」と、カエル従僕は答えました。「明日までな……」

At this moment the door of the house opened, and a large plate came flying out, straight towards the Frog-Footman's head. It hit his nose and then broke into pieces against one of the trees behind him.

"…or the next day, maybe," the Frog-Footman continued as if nothing had happened.

"How can I get in?" Alice asked once again in an even louder voice.

"The first question," said the Frog-Footman, "is—is anyone going to allow you to go in?"

This was certainly an important question but Alice did not like having to think about it.

"It is really terrible," she said to herself, "the way all the animals fight here."

The Frog-Footman continued saying the same things but using different words.

"I will sit here," he said, "on and off, for days and days."

"But what should *I* do?" asked Alice.

"Anything you like," said the Frog-Footman.

"Oh, I don't know why I am talking to him—it won't help me," said Alice to herself. She then opened the door of the house and went in. The door led into a large kitchen which was full of smoke from one end to the other: The Duchess was sitting on a chair in the middle, holding a baby; the cook was standing by the fire, cooking.

■ plate 图 平皿、浅皿　■ come flying out 飛んでくる　■ straight towards 〜に向けてまっすぐ　■ break into pieces 粉々に砕ける　■ on and off 断続的に　■ for days and days 何日も何日も　■ from one end to the other 端から端まで　■ stand by そばに立つ

そのときドアが開き、大きなお皿が従僕の頭をめがけて飛んできました。お皿はカエル従僕の鼻にぶつかり、うしろの木にぶつかって粉々に砕けてしまいました。

「……そうだな、そのまた翌日にしようかなあ」　カエル従僕は、なにごともなかったかのように続けました。

「どうやったら中に入れるんですか？」と、アリスはさらに声を張り上げました。

「最初の質問は、だな」と、カエル従僕は答えました。「つまりじゃな、誰がおまえを中に入れるかってことだな？」

　それはたしかに大問題でしたが、アリスはもうそんなことを考えたくもなかったのです。

「ほんとにひどいわ」と、ひとりごとを言いました。「ここの動物たちって、みんな理屈っぽくて、まったくいやになっちゃう」

　カエル従僕は、言葉を変えて同じことを繰り返しました。

「わしはここに座っているとしよう」と言い、「おったり、おらんかったり、何日も何日もな」

「それじゃあわたしは、いったいどうしたらいいんですか？」と、アリス。

「お好きなように」と、カエル従僕。

「この人と話していてもムダ。何の助けにもならない」と、アリスはつぶやきました。アリスはさっさとドアを開けて中に入りました。ドアは大きな台所につながっていました。すみずみまで煙がもうもうと立ちこめています。公爵夫人は、赤ん坊を抱いて台所の真ん中の椅子に座っていました。料理人がかまどの横に立って料理をしていました。

"There's certainly too much pepper in that soup!" Alice thought. She knew this because she was sneezing.

There certainly was too much pepper in the *air*. Even the Duchess sneezed sometimes; and the baby was sneezing and crying all the time. The only two animals in the kitchen that did *not* sneeze were the cook and a large cat, which was sitting by the fire grinning (smiling).

"Please, would you tell me why your cat grins like that?" asked Alice, a little quietly, for she was not quite sure whether it was polite for her to speak first or not.

"It's a Cheshire-Cat," said the Duchess, "and that's why. Pig!"

Alice jumped when she heard the last word but she soon realised that the Duchess had said that to the baby so Alice felt a lot happier, and she went on speaking.

"I didn't know that Cheshire-Cats always grinned; in fact, I didn't know that cats *could* grin."

"They all can," said the Duchess; "and most of them do."

"I don't know any cats that grin," said Alice very politely, feeling quite pleased that she was having a conversation.

"You don't know much," said the Duchess, "and that's a fact."

■ sneeze 動 くしゃみをする　■ in the air 空中に　■ grin 動 歯を見せてニヤリと笑う
■ whether 接 ～かどうか　■ pleased 形 うれしい

「あのスープ、コショウを入れ過ぎだわ！」と、アリスは思いました。だって、アリスは立て続けにくしゃみをしたからです。
　台所はコショウの匂いで充満していました。公爵夫人さえもときおりくしゃみをしました。赤ちゃんはといえば、くしゃみをしてはひっきりなしに泣きわめいていました。台所でくしゃみをしていないのは、料理人と、かまどの隣に座ってニヤニヤ笑っている大きなネコだけでした。
　「あなたのネコはなぜあんな風にニヤついて（笑って）いるのか、よかったら教えていただけませんか？」と、アリスはひかえめに尋ねました。自分の方から先に口を聞くのは礼儀に反した行為かもしれないと思い、心配だったからです。
　「これはチェシャーネコだからよ」と、公爵夫人が答えました。「だからなのよ。ブタちゃん！」
　最後の言葉を聞いてアリスは飛び上がりました。でも、公爵夫人は赤ん坊に向かって話しかけていることに気づき、かなり気が楽になりました。そして、話を続けることにしました。
　「わたし、チェシャーネコはいつもニヤニヤしているものだってことを、知りませんでした。それに、ネコがニヤニヤ笑いできるなんて、初めて知りました」
　「ネコならみんなニヤつくものよ」と、公爵夫人。「たいていみんなやるわ」
　「わたし、これまでニヤついているネコに会ったことがないんです」アリスはとてもていねいに答えました。会話が成り立っていることがすごくうれしかったのです。
　「あなたはものをあまり知らないわね」と、公爵夫人。「それが事実だわ」

Alice did not like hearing that so she decided to change the subject of the conversation. While she was trying to think of something to talk about, the cook suddenly took the pot off the fire and started throwing everything that she could at the Duchess and the baby. The Duchess didn't move even when the dishes, plates, and pots hit her; and the baby was crying so much already that it was quite impossible to say whether the pots and plates hurt it or not.

"Oh, *please* be careful!" cried Alice, jumping up and down and feeling very worried about the baby.

"If everybody looked after themselves," the Duchess said, "the world would go round faster than it does."

"That would *not* be a good thing," said Alice, who felt very happy to get a chance to show everybody a little of her knowledge. "Just think what work it would make with the day and night! You see the earth takes twenty-four hours to turn round."

"Cut off her head," cried the Duchess.

Alice looked rather worriedly at the cook, to see if she would do what the Duchess had told her to do, but the cook was busy cooking again and did not seem to be listening. So Alice went on talking: "Twenty-four hours, I *think*; or is it twelve? I…"

"Oh, stop talking about numbers," said the Duchess. "I never liked numbers." She then started looking after the baby again.

■ subject 名 話題　■ take the pot off 鍋をおろす　■ impossible 形 不可能な　■ go round ぐるぐる回る　■ get a chance チャンスを得る　■ knowledge 名 知識　■ cut off 切り落とす　■ worriedly 副 心配そうに

雲行きがあやしくなってきたので、アリスは話題を変えることにしました。次の話題を考えていると、料理人が突然鍋を火からおろしたかと思うと、公爵夫人と赤ん坊に向かって、そこらへんにあるものを手当たり次第に投げつけ始めました。公爵夫人は、食器や皿や鍋があたっても、じっと動こうとしませんでした。赤ん坊はといえば、その前からずっとワーワーと泣きわめいていたので、鍋や皿があたって痛くて泣いているのかどうか、さっぱり見当がつきませんでした。

　「まあたいへん、ほんとうにやめてくださいな！」と、アリスは赤ん坊のことをすごく心配して、あちこち飛び回りながら言いました。

　「みんなが自分の面倒をみることができたら」と、公爵夫人が言いました。「地球はもっと早く回転するのにねえ」

　「そんなことになったら大変だわ」と、アリス。自分の知識をちょっとだけ披露できるチャンス到来とばかり、アリスは張り切って言いました。「昼と夜がどうやってできるのか考えてみてくださいな！　だって地球は、24時間かけて回転するんですもの」

　「この子の頭を切り落としておしまい」と、公爵夫人。

　アリスはとても不安になって、料理人の方を見ました。公爵夫人の言いつけに従うつもりかどうか確かめたかったのです。幸い料理人は、まったく聞いていないようで、料理に夢中でした。そこでアリスは、話を続けることにしました。「24時間――たしかそうだと思ったんですけど、あら、それとも12時間だったかしら？　わたし……」

　「数字の話はもうやめなさい」と、公爵夫人。「わたしは昔から数字は大きらいなのよ」　そしてまた、赤ん坊をあやし始めました。

The Duchess started singing to the baby, but, while she was singing, she threw the baby up and down in the air so that it cried even louder. Alice could only just hear what the Duchess was singing.

Soon the Duchess said, "Here! You can hold the baby for a bit, if you like! I must go and get ready to play croquet with the Queen." She hurried out of the room. The cook threw a pot at her as she went, but it just missed the Duchess.

Alice caught the baby with some difficulty, as it was not like a usual baby because it held out its arms and legs in all directions. The baby kept moving so Alice found it very difficult to hold it.

As soon as she had found the best way to hold it, she carried it out into the open air. "If I don't take this baby away with me," thought Alice, "I'm sure they will kill it in a day or two."

The baby started crying again, and Alice looked down into its face to see what the problem was. She saw that it had a very unusual nose (it was much more like a pig's nose than a real nose) and its eyes were very small for a baby's. Alice really did not like looking at it.

"If you are a pig I won't look after you any more," said Alice. The poor little thing started crying again, and Alice walked on in silence.

■ for a bit 少しの間　■ get ready to 〜する準備をする　■ miss 動 当て損なう　■ hold out (腕を)伸ばす　■ out into the open air 戸外へ出る　■ take away 連れて行く　■ in silence 無言で

Chapter VI

　公爵夫人は赤ん坊に子守唄を歌い出しました。でも、歌いながら、赤ん坊を空中に放りあげては受け止めているものですから、赤ん坊は大絶叫しています。アリスには、公爵夫人が何やら歌っている声しか聞こえませんでした。
　すぐに、公爵夫人は言いました。「ほらっ！　よかったらちょっとだけ、赤ん坊を抱かせてあげましょう！　わたしは女王陛下とクロッケーのゲームをする支度をしなくちゃならないからね」　赤ん坊を放り投げた公爵夫人は、さっさと台所を出て行ってしまいました。料理人は、そのうしろ姿に向かって、鍋をピューンと投げつけましたが、ぎりぎりのところで公爵夫人には命中しませんでした。
　アリスはなんとか赤ん坊を抱きとめましたが、それからがとても大変でした。だってこの子は、ふつうの赤ん坊ではなかったのです。両手両足を思いっきりあちこちに付き出していました。しょっちゅう動くので、抱きとめていることさえ一苦労でした。
　やっと赤ん坊を抱くコツを覚えたアリスは、赤ん坊を抱いて外に出ました。「わたしがこの子と一緒にここから抜け出さなかったら」と、アリスは考えました。「連中は絶対に、この子をほんの一日かそこらで始末してしまうわ」
　赤ん坊はまた泣き出しました。アリスは赤ん坊の顔をのぞき込んで、いったいどうしたのか確かめようとしました。すると、赤ん坊がとても変わった鼻をしていることに気づきました（ホンモノの鼻というより、ブタの鼻に近かったのです）。おまけにこの子の目といったら、赤ん坊にしては異常に小さかったのです。アリスは、これ以上この子の顔を見ているのはいやになってしまいました。
　「もしあなたがブタなら、もうあなたのお世話はしませんからね」と、アリス。かわいそうな赤ん坊は、また泣き出しました。アリスは黙りこくって歩き続けました。

Alice was just beginning to think to herself, "Now, what am I to do with this animal when I get it home?" It then cried again so loudly that she looked down into its face, feeling afraid. This time there could be *no* mistake. The baby was a pig, not a baby, and she felt that it would be silly for her to carry it any more.

So she put the little animal down and felt very happy to see it walk away quietly into the wood. "If it had grown up," she said to herself, "it would not have been a pretty child: but it is a very nice pig." And then she began thinking about other children she knew who might be very good as pigs. At that moment, she was very surprised to see the Cheshire-Cat sitting in a tree near her.

The Cat only grinned when it saw Alice. It looked kind, she thought: but it had a *great* many teeth, so she felt she should be nice to it.

"Cheshire-Cat," she began, rather quietly, as she did not know if it would like the name. It grinned a little more.

"It's happy," thought Alice, so she went on. "Would you tell me, please, which way I should go from here?"

■ get someone home （人）を連れて帰る　■ look down into 〜を覗き込む　■ silly 形 ばかげた　■ be nice to （人）に良くする

Chapter VI

　アリスは思いをめぐらせていました。「おうちに連れて帰ったら、この子をどうしましょう！」 そのとき、その子はものすごい音を出して叫んだので、アリスはこわごわ顔をのぞき込みました。今度こそ、絶対に間違いありません。赤ん坊は、ブタで、人間の赤ちゃんではありませんでした。アリスは、このままブタを抱っこしているなんて、やっぱりおかしいと思いました。

　そこで子ブタを地面に下ろしました。子ブタがおとなしくトコトコと森の中に歩いて行く姿を見とどけ、アリスは心底ホッとしました。「あの子が大きくなったら」と、アリスはつぶやきました。「カワイイ子どもにはならないでしょうね。でも、きっとハンサムなブタちゃんになるわ」 そしてアリスは、知っている子どもたちのことを思い浮かべました。あの子たちも、ブタだったら、きっとカワイイのになあと思いました。その時、驚いたことに、あのチェシャーネコが、アリスのすぐそばの木の枝の上に座っているのが見えました。

　ネコはアリスを見て、ニヤッとしました。それを見てアリスは、やさしそうなネコみたいな気がしました。でも、ものすごくたくさんの歯が見えたので、ていねいに接した方がよさそうだと感じました。

　「チェシャーネコさん」と、アリスはおずおずと切り出しました。そう呼びかけていいのかどうかわからなかったからです。ネコはニヤッと笑いを大きくしました。

　「機嫌がよさそうだわ」と思い、アリスは続けました。「教えていただきたいんですが、わたしこれから、どこに向かったらいいのでしょうか？」

"The important question is, where do you want to go to," said the Cat.

"I don't really care where…" said Alice.

"Then it doesn't matter which way you go," said the Cat.

"…so long as I get *somewhere*," Alice added.

"Oh, you're sure to do that," said the Cat, "if you walk far enough."

Alice felt that this was true, so she tried another question. "What sort of people live here?"

"In *that* direction," the Cat said, pointing to the right, "lives a Hatter: and in *that* direction," pointing to the left, "lives a March Hare. You can visit either of them; they are both mad."

"But I don't want to go and see mad people," said Alice.

"Oh, but you have to," said the Cat, "because we are all mad here. I'm mad. You're mad."

"How do you know I'm mad?" asked Alice.

"You must be," replied the Cat, "or you wouldn't have come here."

Alice didn't believe that but she continued, "and how do you know that you're mad?"

"To begin with," said the Cat, "a dog's not mad. Do you agree with that?"

"I suppose so," said Alice.

"Well then," the Cat said, "you see a dog barks when it's angry and moves its tail when it's pleased. Now *I* bark when I'm pleased and move my tail when I'm angry. Therefore, I'm mad."

■ so long as ～さえすれば ■ hatter 名 帽子屋 ■ hare 名 野ウサギ
■ mad 形 気が狂って ■ to begin with まず、そもそも ■ agree with （人）に同意する
■ therefore 副 だから

「重要な質問は、あんたがどこへ行きたいかだよ」と、ネコが答えました。

「別にどこへ行ってもいいんです」と、アリス。

「それならどこへ行ったっていいじゃないか」と、ネコ。

「どこかへたどり着くことさえできれば」と、アリス。

「それは問題ないよ」と、ネコは続けました。「遠くまで行けばいい」

その答えに納得したアリスは、次の質問をしました。「ここにはどんな人たちが住んでるんですか？」

「あっちのほうには」と、ネコは右の方をさして言いました。「帽子屋が住んでいる。それからこっちには」と、左の方向をさして、「三月ウサギが住んでる。どっちを訪ねてもいい。二人ともイカレているがね」

「でもわたし、イカレた人たちには会いたくありません」と、アリスは答えました。

「いいや。会いに行かねばならぬ」と、ネコは言いました。「ここにいる連中はみーんな、イカレてるからな。おれも、おまえさんもな」

「わたしがイカレてるなんて、どうしてわかるんですか？」と、アリスは尋ねました。

「それは決まってる」と、ネコは答えました。「でなきゃこんなところに来るはずがない」

そんなおかしな話は信じられないと思いましたが、質問を続けることにしました。「それに、どうしてあなたは、自分がイカレてるってわかるんですか？」

「いいか」と、ネコ。「イヌはイカレていない。同感だろ？」

「ええ、たぶん」と、アリス。

「それなら」と、ネコは続けます。「イヌは怒ったら吠えるし、機嫌がいいときにはしっぽを振る。ところで、おれの場合には、怒ったらしっぽを振るし、上機嫌のときには吠える。だからおれは、イカレてるんだよ」

"But cats don't bark—only dogs do," said Alice.

"That doesn't make any difference," said the Cat. "Are you going to play croquet with the Queen today?"

"I would very much like to play," said Alice, "but she hasn't asked me yet."

"You'll see me there," said the Cat, and it disappeared. Alice was not very surprised that he had disappeared, because strange things were always happening. While she was still looking at the place where it had been, it suddenly appeared again.

"I just wondered what happened to the baby?" asked the Cat. "I'd nearly forgotten to ask."

"It was a pig," Alice answered very quietly so that the Cat did not feel that she was surprised that he had come back.

"I thought it would be," said the Cat, and then he disappeared again.

Alice waited a little, not sure if he would come back again or not, but it did not reappear, and after a minute or two she walked on in the direction in which the Cat had said the March Hare lived. "I've seen Hatters before," she said to herself, "the March Hare will be much the most interesting, and perhaps because this is May he won't be as mad as he was in March."

■ not very あまり〜しない　■ reappear 動 再び現れる

「お言葉ですが、ネコは吠えないと思います——吠えるのはイヌだけでしょう」と、アリス。
　「そんなことはどっちだってよい」と、ネコ。「おまえさん今日、女王陛下と一緒にクロッケーのゲームをすんのかい?」
　「ぜひそうしたいんですが」と、アリスは答えました。「でもまだ陛下から招待されていないんです」
　「じゃ、そこでまた会おう」と言ったかと思うと、ネコはふっと消えてしまいました。ネコが消えてもアリスはもう驚きませんでした。だって、次々と不思議なことが立て続けに起こっていたからです。アリスはしばらくネコがいた場所を見つめていました。すると突然、あのネコがまた現れました。
　「赤ん坊はどうなったんだい?」と、ネコは尋ねました。「もうちょっとで聞き忘れるところだった」
　「あれはブタでした」と、アリスは大急ぎで答えました。ネコがもどってきてアリスが驚いているんだと、ネコに思われたくなかったからです。
　「そんなことだと思ったよ」と言って、ネコはまたふっと消えてしまいました。
　またネコがもどってくるかどうかわからなかったので、アリスは少しだけ待ちました。ネコはもどってきませんでした。1、2分してからアリスは、三月ウサギが住んでいるとネコが教えてくれた方向に歩きだしました。「わたし、帽子屋さんには会ったことがあるわ」とつぶやき、「三月ウサギの方がずっとおもしろそうだわ。それに、今はもう5月だから、3月ほどイカレていないかもしれないわ」

As she said this, she looked up and saw the Cat again sitting in the tree.

"Did you say 'pig'?" said the Cat.

"Yes, I did," replied Alice, "and I wish you wouldn't keep appearing and disappearing."

"All right," said the Cat; and this time it disappeared quite slowly, beginning with its tail. The last thing that disappeared was its grin.

"Well, I've often seen a cat without a grin," thought Alice; "but a grin without a cat! It's the strangest thing I have ever seen!"

She had not gone far before she saw the March Hare's house. It was such a large house that she did not want to go near it until she had eaten some more of the left-hand piece of the mushroom and made herself about two feet high. Even then, she walked up towards it rather slowly, saying to herself, "I hope it is not mad today! I almost wish I'd gone to see the Hatter instead!"

■ begin with 〜から始まる　■ left-hand 形 左手の、左側の　■ even then それでも

そう言いながらふと見上げると、ネコがまた木の枝にとまっているのが見えました。
　「ブタって言った？」と、ネコ。
　「ええ。そう言いました」と、アリスは答えました。「突然消えたり、また現れたりするのをやめていただけたら、わたしうれしいんですけど」
　「了解」とネコは言って、今度はすごくゆっくりと、しっぽの先から順番に消えていきました。最後に消えたのは、ニヤニヤ笑いでした。
　「ニヤッとしないネコはたくさん知っているけど」と、アリスは思いました。「でも、ネコなしのニヤッなんて！　今までで一番不思議な光景だわ！」
　少ししたら、三月ウサギの家が見えてきました。それはものすごく大きな家でした。アリスは、左に持っていたキノコのかけらを少しかじり、60センチぐらいの身長になってからその家に近づくことにしました。そして歩調をゆるめながら、アリスは家に近づいていきました。こんなひとりごとをつぶやきました。「今日のウサギはイカレてなければいいけど！　帽子屋さんの方にしておけばよかったのかしら！」

Chapter VII

A Mad Tea-Party

There was a table set out under a tree in front of the house, and the March Hare and the Hatter were having tea at it.

A Dormouse was sitting between them, asleep, and the other two were resting their arms on its shoulders and were talking over its head. "Not very nice for the Dormouse," thought Alice; "but, as it is asleep, I suppose it feels alright."

The table was a large one, but the three of them were all sitting at one end of it. "No room! No room!" they cried out when they saw Alice coming.

"There's *lots* of room," said Alice and she sat down in a large chair at one end of the table.

"Have some orange juice," said the March Hare in a friendly way.

■ set out 配置する ■ have tea お茶を飲む ■ dormouse 名 ヤマネ ■ asleep 形 眠って ■ over one's head 頭越しに ■ at one end of ～の一方の端に ■ cry out 叫ぶ、大声を上げる

第 7 章

クレイジーお茶会

　家の前の木かげにはテーブルが置かれていました。そこで三月ウサギと帽子屋が紅茶を飲んでいました。
　ヤマネが2人の間に座ってぐっすり眠りこけています。他の2人はヤマネの肩に肘をつき、その頭ごしに話しこんでいます。「ヤマネがかわいそうだわ」と、アリスは思いました。「でも、眠っているから平気なのかもしれないわね」

　大きなテーブルでしたが、3人はそのはじっこにひと固まりになって座っていました。「席はないよ！　席はないよ！」と、2人はアリスがやってくるのを見ると、叫びました。
　「たっぷりあいてるじゃないの」と言って、アリスはテーブルのはしに置かれた大きな椅子に腰かけました。
　「オレンジジュースをどうぞ」と、三月ウサギがやさしい口調で言いました。

Alice looked all round the table, but there was nothing on it except tea.

"I can't see any orange juice," she said.

"There isn't any," said the March Hare.

"Then it wasn't very polite of you to offer it," said Alice angrily.

"It wasn't very polite of you to sit down without us saying that you could," said the March Hare.

"I didn't know it was *your* table," said Alice, "there are plates and cups for many more than three people."

"Your hair should be cut," said the Hatter. He had been looking at Alice for some time with great interest, but this was his first speech.

"You should learn not to say things about people," said Alice: "it's very impolite."

The Hatter opened his eyes very wide when he heard this, but all he *said* was, "What day of the month is it?" He had taken his watch out of his coat, and was looking at it, shaking it every now and then and holding it near his ear.

Alice thought for a minute, and then said, "It's the fourth."

"Two days wrong!" said the Hatter. "I told you butter would not be good for my watch!" he added, looking angrily at the March Hare.

"It was the *best* butter," said the March Hare quietly.

"Yes, but some bread must have got in to the watch as well," the Hatter said: "You should not have used the bread-knife to put the butter in my watch."

■ except 前 ～を除いて ■ every now and then 時々 ■ butter 图 バター ■ as well おまけに ■ bread-knife 图 パン切りナイフ

アリスがテーブルを見わたすと、紅茶しか見あたりません。
「オレンジジュースなんて、ないんですけど」と、アリス。
「そんなものないよ」と、三月ウサギ。
「ないものをどうぞって勧めるなんて、失礼だわ」と、アリスはぷりぷりして言いました。
「どうぞおかけくださいって言われる前に座るなんて、失礼だ」と、三月ウサギが言い返します。
「あなたがたのテーブルだってこと、知らなかったんですもの」と、アリス。「それに、ここには3人以上のお皿やカップがおいてあるわ」
「ヘアカットが必要だね」と、帽子屋が言いました。さっきから興味しんしん、アリスを見つめていましたが、最初の一言がこれだったのです。
「ひとのことをとやかく言うのはよくないわ」と、アリス。「すごく失礼ですもの」
帽子屋はそれを聞いて、眼をまんまるに見開きました。でも、口から出てきた言葉は、「今日は何日だったっけ？」そして上着から時計を取り出してながめ、ときおり時計を振ったり、耳にあてたりしました。

アリスは1分ほど考えてから、言いました。「4日よ」
「2日違う！」と、帽子屋。「バターは時計にあわないって言っただろう！」と、三月ウサギを腹立たしげににらんで言いました。
「サイコーのバターだったんだよ」と、三月ウサギはせかせかと答えました。
「ただし、パンくずも時計に入り込んでしまったようだな」と、帽子屋。「パン切りナイフでおれの時計にバターをぬりこんだりしちゃあいけなかったんだよ」

The March Hare took the watch and looked at it sadly: Then he put it into his cup of tea, and looked at it again: But he could think of nothing better to say than what he had said at first, "It was the best butter you know."

Alice had been looking at him with some interest. "What a funny watch!" she said. "It shows the day of the month, but it doesn't say what time it is!"

"Why should it?" said the Hatter. "Does *your* watch tell you what year it is?"

"Of course not," replied Alice: "But that is because it stays the same year for such a long time."

"That is the same with *my* watch," said the Hatter.

Alice didn't understand at all. What the Hatter had said seemed to have no meaning in it, but she knew that it was certainly English. "I don't quite understand you," she said as politely as she could.

"The Dormouse is asleep again," said the Hatter, and he poured a little hot tea upon its nose. The Dormouse shook its head and said, without opening its eyes, "Of course, of course: just what I was going to say myself."

"I think you might do something better with your time," Alice said, "than saying things that have no meaning."

"'Time' is '*him*' not '*it*'!" said the Hatter.

"I don't know what you mean," said Alice.

■ funny 形 おかしな ■ have no meaning 無意味である ■ pour 動 ～を注ぐ

三月ウサギは情けなさそうな顔で時計を見つめました。それから、紅茶が入った自分のティーカップの中にちゃぽんとひたし、もう一度時計をながめました。最初に言ったことよりもましなことを思いつきませんでした。「サイコーのバターだったのになあ」

　アリスは好奇心まんまんでウサギを見ていました。「なんておかしな時計なんでしょう！」と、アリス。「何日かわかるけど、時間がわからないわね！」

　「それで何がおかしい？」と、帽子屋。「あんたの時計は何年かわかるのかい？」

　「もちろんわからないわ」と、アリスは返事しました。「だって、一年間はとっても長くて変わらないからよ」

　「おれの時計だっておんなじさ」と、帽子屋。

　アリスにはわけがわかりませんでした。帽子屋が言っていることはまったく意味不明に思えましたが、英語で話していることだけは確かでした。「ちょっと理解しかねるのですが」と、できるだけていねいに言いました。

　「ヤマネがまた寝ちゃった」と、帽子屋は言い、熱い紅茶をヤマネの鼻の上にたらしました。ヤマネは頭をふると、目をつぶったまま言いました。「とうぜん、とうぜん、ぼくも今、そう言おうとしていたとこ」

　「もっと賢く時間を使うべきだと思うわ」と、アリスは言いました。「意味のないことばかり言っていないで」

　「時間は"彼"で、"それ"ではない！」と、帽子屋。

　「わけがわからないわ」と、アリス。

"Of course you don't!" the Hatter said. "I guess you have never spoken to 'Time'!"

"No, I haven't," replied Alice.

"Ah, that explains it," said the Hatter. "If you were friendly with 'Time' he would do almost anything you liked with the clock. For example, if it were nine o'clock in the morning and it was time to begin your lessons, you would only have to speak quietly to him ('Time') and the clock would move on very quickly to half past one—time for dinner!"

("I only wish it was," the March Hare said to itself quietly.)

"That would certainly be wonderful," said Alice thoughtfully: "but then I would not be hungry for lunch."

"Not at first, perhaps," said the Hatter, "but you could keep the clock at half past one for as long as you liked."

"Is that what *you* do?" asked Alice.

The Hatter shook his head unhappily. "No, I don't!" he replied. "We talked angrily to each other last March—just before *he* became mad…" (pointing to the March Hare), "…it was when we all went to sing songs with the Queen of Hearts, and I had to sing:

"Twinkle, twinkle little thing
How I wonder what you're doing!"

■ half past one　1時半　■ thoughtfully 副 考え深く　■ as long as 〜する限り

「わかるわけがないよ！」と、帽子屋。「"時間クン"と話したことがないだろうからな！」

「そのとおりよ」と、アリス。

「ああ、それでわかったぞ」と、帽子屋。「"時間クン"と仲良くなれば、"彼"は、時計をあんたの好きなように変えてくれる。たとえば、朝9時になって、授業が始まる時間だとする。彼（時間クン）にそっとささやくだけで、時計の針はあっという間にぐるりとまわって1時半をさしてくれる——ディナータイムだ！」

（「ああ、そうだといいのに」と、三月ウサギはささっとつぶやきました。）

「たしかにそれは素敵よね」と、アリスはじっと考えながら言いました。「ただ、それだと、わたしまだお腹がすいてないんじゃないかしら」

「最初はそうかもしれない」と、帽子屋。「でも、時計の針をずっと好きなだけ1時半にしておけばいいんだよ」

「そんなこと、あなたはほんとうにやっているの？」と、アリスは尋ねました。

帽子屋は悲しそうに首を横にふって、「いいや。やっていない」と、答えました。「おれと時間クンは、去年の3月に口げんかしちゃってね。彼がオカシくなる直前だった……」（三月ウサギを指差しながら）、「……ハートの女王様主催の大コンサートにみんなで参加したときのことだった。おれが歌わなきゃならなかったのは、

　　「きらきらおちびちゃん、
　　　　いったい今ごろ何してるん！」

"There is more of the song you know," said the Hatter. "It's like this."

> *"Up above the world you fly,*
> *Like a tea-tray in the sky."*

The Dormouse suddenly shook itself and began singing "*Twinkle, Twinkle*" in its sleep. It went on singing for so long that they had to hit it to make it stop.

"I had not finished my song," said the Hatter, "when the Queen suddenly became very angry and cried out 'Off with his Head'!"

"How terrible!" cried Alice.

"And ever since then," said the Hatter in a sad voice, "he won't do anything I ask him to do! It's always six o'clock now."

A good idea came into Alice's head. "Is that the reason why so many tea things are on the table?" she asked.

"Yes, that's it," said the Hatter, "it's always tea-time here, and we have no time to wash the things."

"So you keep moving round the table, I suppose?" said Alice.

"Yes, that is right," said the Hatter.

"But what happens when you come to the beginning again?" asked Alice.

■ tea-tray 图 茶盆　■ for so long 長い間　■ Off with one's head! 首をはねよ！《＝Cut one's head off!》　■ ever since then それ以後ずっと　■ tea things 茶道具

「歌の続きを知ってるよね」と、帽子屋。「こんな感じだよ」

　　　「天高く、飛べよ飛べ、
　　　　　お空の茶盆のように、飛べよ飛べ」

　ここでヤマネはぶるっと身ぶるいして、眠りながら「きらきら」と歌い出しました。いつまでたってもやめないので、みんなで頭をたたいてやめさせました。
「まだおれの歌は終わっていなかったんだ」と、帽子屋。「女王陛下が突如として怒りだし、『彼の首を落としておしまい！』と叫んだのさ」
「まあ、なんてひどい！」と、アリスは大声をあげました。
「それからというもの」と、帽子屋は沈んだ声で続けました。「彼は決しておれの言うことを聞いてくれなくなったんだ！　おかげでいつも、いま6時」
　そのとき、アリスはぱっとひらめきました。「わかった。それで、テーブルの上にはこんなに一杯お茶の道具が並んでいるの？」と、アリスは尋ねました。
「正解」と、帽子屋。「ここではいつもティータイム。食器を洗う暇もないんだよ」
「だから順々に席をずらしてテーブルの周りをまわっているのね？」と、アリス。
「正解」と、帽子屋。
「でもぐるっとまわって、もとの場所にもどったら、どうするの？」と、アリスは聞いてみました。

"Why don't we talk about something else?" said the March Hare. "I'm getting tired of this. I think this young lady should tell us a story."

"I'm afraid I don't know one," said Alice, rather worried about the idea of telling a story.

"Then the Dormouse will!" they both cried. "Wake up, Dormouse!" they shouted. The Dormouse slowly opened its eyes. "I wasn't asleep," it said, "I heard every word you said."

"Tell us a story," said the March Hare.

"Yes, please do!" added Alice.

"And be quick about it," added the Hatter, "or you will be asleep again before you have finished it."

"Once upon a time there were three little sisters," the Dormouse began quickly; "and their names were Elsie, Lacie and Tillie; and they lived at the bottom of a hole…"

"What did they eat?" said Alice, who always took a great interest in questions of eating and drinking.

"They ate treacle," said the Dormouse after thinking for a minute or two.

"They couldn't have done that," Alice said quietly. "They would have been ill."

"They were," said the Dormouse, "they were *very* ill."

■ Why don't we ～しませんか？　■ wake up 目を覚ます　■ once upon a time むかしむかし　■ treacle 图 糖蜜　■ ill 形 病気で

「話題を変えないか？」と、三月ウサギが口をはさみました。「もう飽きた。このお嬢さんに、なにかお話をしてもらおうじゃないか」

「ごめんなさい。お話なんて、わたし一つも知らないんです」と、アリスは、この提案にどぎまぎして言いました。

「それならヤマネ、お前がやれ！」と、帽子屋と三月ウサギが一緒に叫びました。「起きろよ、ヤマネ！」ヤマネはのろのろと目を開き、「寝てないよ〜」と、言いました。「ぜ〜んぶ、ちゃんと聞いてたからね」

「お話をしてくれ」と、三月ウサギ。

「お願いします！」と、アリス。

「さっさと始めろよ」と、帽子屋。「さもなきゃお話が終わる前に、おまえ、またコトンと眠っちゃうだろ」

「むかしむかし、3人の姉妹がいました」と、ヤマネはあわててお話を始めました。「名前は、エルシー、レイシー、ティリーでした。3人は深い穴の底に住んでいました……」

「何を食べていたの？」と、アリスは尋ねました。日ごろから、食べたり飲んだりすることには人一倍興味があったからです。

「姉妹は糖蜜を食べて生きていました」と、ヤマネは1、2分考えてから答えました。

「そんなの無理よ」と、すかさずアリスは言いました。「だってそれじゃ病気になっちゃうわ」

「姉妹は病気だったのです」と、ヤマネ。「すご〜く重い病気にかかっていました」

Alice tried to think what it would be like only eating treacle but she could not so she asked, "Why did they live at the bottom of a hole?"

"Take some more tea," the March Hare told Alice.

"I haven't had any tea," Alice replied, "so I can't take any more." She decided that the easiest thing to do was to take some tea and bread and butter for herself because she did not think they would give her anything, and then she turned to the Dormouse and asked him her question again. "Why did they live at the bottom of a hole?"

The Dormouse again took a minute or two to think about it and then said, "It was a treacle-hole."

"There's no such thing!" said Alice. She was beginning to get very angry, but the Hatter and the March Hare went "Sh! Sh!" and the Dormouse said, "If you can't be polite, you should finish the story for yourself."

"No, please go on!" Alice said. "I won't say anything more." The Dormouse agreed to go on.

"And so these three little sisters—they were learning to draw…"

"What did they draw?" said Alice, already forgetting her promise not to say anything more.

"Treacle," said the Dormouse.

"I want a clean cup," the Hatter suddenly said, "let's all move on one place."

■ bread and butter バター付きパン ■ for oneself 自力で ■ move on one place 一つずれる

Chapter VII

　アリスは、糖蜜だけで生きていくことをいろいろと想像してみましたが、やはり無理でした。かわりに、「なぜ姉妹は深い穴の底で暮らしていたの？」と、質問しました。

　「お茶のお代わりはいかが？」と、三月ウサギはアリスに言いました。

　「わたし、まだお茶をいただいていないんですけど」と、アリスは答えました。「だからお代りはできません」　そこでアリスは考えました。紅茶をいただいて、バターを塗ったパンをさっさと食べてしまうのが、一番てっとり早いと。だって、だれもアリスにお茶を注いでくれそうな人はここにはいなかったからです。次にアリスは、ヤマネに向かって質問を繰り返しました。「なぜ姉妹は深い穴の底で暮らしていたの？」

　ヤマネはまた1、2分考えてから答えました。「それは、糖蜜の穴だったのです」

　「そんなのあるわけないでしょ！」と言って、アリスはすごく腹がたってきました。でも、帽子屋と三月ウサギに、「シーッ！　シーッ！」と言われてしまいました。次にヤマネは言いました。「おとなしく聞いていられないんだったら、自分で最後まで話したらどうだい」

　「とんでもない。どうぞ続けてください！」と、アリス。「もう黙っていますから」　ヤマネはお話を続けることにしました。

　「そして、3人の幼い姉妹は、お絵かきの勉強を始めました……」

　「なんの絵を描いたの？」と、アリスは、たった今、黙っているという約束をしたことをすっかり忘れて言いました。

　「糖蜜だ」と、ヤマネ。

　「きれいなカップがほしいな」と、帽子屋が突然言い出しました。「いっこずつ、場所をずれよう」

As he spoke he started to move to the next seat, and the Dormouse followed him: the March Hare moved into the Dormouse's place, and Alice rather unwillingly took the March Hare's seat.

The Hatter was the only one who did well from the move as he had a clean cup. Alice was in a worse place as the March Hare had put milk onto his plate.

Alice did not want to make the Dormouse unhappy again, so she began very carefully: "But I don't understand. Why did they draw treacle?"

"They were learning to draw," the Dormouse said in a sleepy voice because he was getting very tired. "They drew all kinds of things—everything that begins with an 'M'."

"Why with an 'M'?" said Alice.

"Why not?" said the March Hare.

Alice was silent. The Dormouse had closed its eyes by this time and was falling asleep, but the Hatter suddenly hit it so it woke up and it went on with its story.

"…words that begin with an 'M,' such as the moon, milk, and men."

■ unwillingly 副 嫌々　■ do well うまくいく　■ such as 例えば〜など

そう言いながら、帽子屋は隣の席へ動き始め、ヤマネもそれに続きました。三月ウサギはヤマネのいた席に移動し、アリスはしぶしぶ、三月ウサギのいた席に移動しました。

　この席替えで得をしたのは、帽子屋だけでした。だって移動したおかげで、きれいなカップの前に座ることができたからです。アリスの席は最悪でした。三月ウサギがお皿の上にミルクをこぼしてしまっていたからです。

　アリスは、さっきみたいにヤマネの機嫌を損ねないよう、遠慮がちに質問しました。「あのう、わたし、どうしてもわからないんですけど。なぜ3姉妹は、糖蜜の絵を描いたのですか？」

　「絵の勉強を始めたからだよ」と、ヤマネは眠そうに言いました。かなりくたびれてきたからです。「姉妹はいろいろなものを描いていた。ぜんぶ、Mの頭文字で始まるものをね」

　「なぜMなの？」と、アリス。

　「Mでなぜ悪い？」と、三月ウサギ。

　アリスは黙ってしまいました。ヤマネはついに目を閉じ、うとうとし始めていました。でも帽子屋にひっぱたかれて目をさまし、お話を続けました。

　「……Mのつく言葉は、ムーン（月）とか、ミルクとか、メン（男性）とかある」

Alice then decided to leave the party because she felt they were very impolite to her and she did not like the fact that the Dormouse kept falling asleep. Nobody noticed her leaving, though she looked back once or twice, half hoping that they would call after her; the last time she saw them they were trying to put the Dormouse into the teapot.

"I'll certainly never go *there* again!" said Alice as she walked through the wood. "It is the maddest tea-party I have ever been to!"

Just as she said this, she noticed that one of the trees had a door in it. "That's very strange!" she thought. "But everything is strange today. I think I will go through this door and see what happens." So in she went.

Once more she found herself in the long hall, and close to the little glass table. "Now, I'll do better this time," she said to herself, and began by taking the little golden key, and opening the door that led into the garden. Then she started eating the mushroom so that she would become small enough to walk down towards the garden. At last she got there and found herself in a beautiful garden with a lot of lovely flowers and cool water.

■ So in she went. 《副詞を文頭に置く倒置「副詞＋S＋V」》　■ do better　よりよくやる

Chapter VII

　アリスは、そろそろ、おいとまする時間が来たと思いました。だって、みんなアリスに対してとてもぶしつけだったし、ヤマネが居眠りばかりしているのが気にくわなかったのです。アリスがテーブルを離れても、誰も気づきませんでした。みんなでアリスを呼びもどそうとしてくれるかもしれないと、ちょっとだけ期待して、1、2度振り返ってみたのですが、だれも気づいてくれませんでした。最後に振り返ったときには、2人でヤマネをティーポットの中に押し込もうとしているのが見えました。

「もう二度とあそこへは行かないわ！」と、アリスは森の中を歩きながら思いました。「今までで一番、クレイジーなお茶会だったわ！」
　そう口にした瞬間、ある木の幹に扉が付いているのに気づきました。「まあ、不思議！」と、アリスは思いました。「でも、今日は何もかも不思議だらけだから、ここを抜けてみようかしら」　そして、アリスは扉の中に入りました。

　またしてもアリスは、あの細長い広間にいました。小さなガラスのテーブルのそばに立っていました。「今度こそ、うまくやるわ」と、つぶやき、手始めに、小さな金色の鍵をつかんで、お庭に通じる扉を開けました。次に、キノコを食べて、庭に向かって歩いていけるだけの大きさにまで身長を縮めました。とうとうアリスは、成功しました。花々がまぶしく咲き乱れ、冷たいお水が流れる、あの素晴らしいお庭に出ることができたのです。

Chapter VIII

The Queen's Croquet Ground

A large rose-tree stood near the entrance of the garden; the roses growing on it were white, but three gardeners (people who work in a garden) wearing playing cards were busily painting the roses red. Alice thought this was a very strange thing to be doing so she went nearer to watch them. When she got close she heard one of them say, "Be careful, Five! Don't paint me!"

"I'm sorry," said Five, "but Seven hit my arm." They started talking about this and suddenly noticed Alice watching them. They all turned round to look at her and bowed low.

"Would you tell me, please," said Alice, a little quietly, "why you are painting those roses?"

■ gardener 名 庭師　■ get close 近づく

第 8 章
女王陛下のクロッケー競技場

　お庭の入口の近くには、大きなバラの木が一本立っていました。その木には白いバラの花が咲いていました。でも、トランプの服を着た3人の庭師が、せっせと白バラたちを赤く染めていました。ずいぶんとヘンなことをするものだと思い、アリスは近づいて観察することにしました。そばまで行くと、庭師の一人が、「おい5番、オレにペンキを塗るつもりか！」と言っているのが聞こえました。

　「すまん」と、5番が言いました。「でもなあ、7番がオレの腕にぶつかってきたんだよ」　みんなで話し始めたとき、3人は、アリスが自分たちを見ていることに気づきました。庭師たちはアリスの方を振り向き、深々とお辞儀をしました。
　「教えていただけませんでしょうか？」と、アリスはひかえめに尋ねました。「みなさんはなぜ、バラを赤く染めていらっしゃるのですか？」

Five and Seven said nothing but looked at Two (another playing card gardener.) Two began in a low voice, "Well, you see, Miss, this tree should have been a *red* rose-tree but we put a white one here. If the Queen knew this was a white rose-tree she would cut our heads off. So we are trying to make it look red before she comes to—" At that moment, Five, who had been looking round the garden, called out "The Queen! The Queen!" and then the three gardeners lay down on the ground. Alice heard the sound of lots of people so she looked round because she wanted to see the Queen.

She could see a lot of people—all wearing playing cards like the gardeners. First the servants came and then the guards. They were followed by the Queen's children. There were ten of them. Then the guests came—they were mostly Kings and Queens and Alice saw the White Rabbit with them. It was talking and smiling so much that it walked past Alice without seeing her. Finally the Knave came (he was the King and Queen of Hearts' son) and, last of all, the King and Queen of Hearts.

Alice did not know what to do. She thought she should lie down like the gardeners but if she did she would not be able to see anything. So she stood where she was and waited.

When they came near her, they all stopped and looked at her, and the Queen asked, "Who is this?" She said it to the Knave of Hearts but he only bowed and smiled. No one replied.

So the Queen said to Alice, "What's your name, child?"

■ lie down ひれ伏す　■ walk past ～の横を通り過ぎる　■ Knave 图 (トランプの) ジャック　■ last of all 最後に

Chapter VIII

　5番と7番は無言で2番（もう一人の庭師）の方を見ました。2番は低い声で話し始めました。「お嬢ちゃん、いいかね。この木はもともと赤いバラの木のはずだったんだよ。でも間違えて白バラの木を植えてしまったんだ。もし女王陛下が白バラの木を植えたとお知りになったら、我々の首はすっ飛んでしまう。だから、陛下がいらっしゃる前に、せっせと赤に塗り変えていたんだよ——」そのとき、お庭を見わたしていた5番が叫びました。「女王陛下だ！　女王陛下だ！」　そして3人は、地面にひれふしました。大勢の足音が聞こえてきました。女王陛下の姿を一目見ようと思い、アリスはあたりを見わたしました。

　庭師たちのようにトランプの服を着ている人が大勢いるのが見えました。先頭は、廷臣たちで、その次が護衛兵、そして次が女王陛下の子どもたちでした。子どもは全部で10人いました。それから、お客さまたち。たいていは王様や女王様でした。その中に白ウサギがまじっているのにアリスは気づきました。白ウサギはしゃべったり、ほほ笑むのに大忙しで、アリスに気づきもしないで通り過ぎていきました。次に、ハートのジャックが行進して来ました（彼は、ハートの王様と女王陛下の息子でした）。そしてこの大行列の一番最後を飾るのは、ハートの王様と女王陛下でした。

　アリスはどうしてよいかわかりませんでした。庭師たちのように地面にひれふそうかとも思いましたが、そんなことをしたら、何も見えなくなるので、立ったまま、行列を待ちかまえることにしました。

　行列がアリスのそばに来たとき、一同は止まって、アリスを見つめました。女王陛下が尋ねました。「これは何者か？」　そう尋ねられたハートのジャックは、ただお辞儀をしてほほ笑みました。返事をするものは誰もいませんでした。

　そこで女王陛下は、アリスに向かって尋ねました。「名前はなんというのか、そこの子ども？」

"My name is Alice," said Alice very politely, but she realised they were all only a pack of playing cards so she decided she didn't need to be afraid of them.

"And who are *these*?" asked the Queen pointing to the three gardeners who were lying round the rose-tree. She did not know who they were because they were lying on their front, and the backs of all the cards looked the same.

"Why do you think *I* know?" said Alice feeling very strong.

The Queen turned red with anger and began shouting, "Off with her head! Off with—"

"That's mad!" said Alice very loudly and decidedly, and the Queen was silent.

The King put his hand on her arm and said, "My dear, she is only a child!" The Queen turned angrily away from him and then she told the gardeners to get up. They jumped up and began bowing to the King, the Queen, the Royal children and everybody else.

"Stop that!" cried the Queen. And then she asked the gardeners what they were doing.

■ a pack of 〜の一包み　■ playing card トランプ　■ lie on one's front うつぶせに寝る　■ turn red 顔を赤くする　■ my dear あなた、ねえ君《愛する人への呼びかけ》

「わたしの名前はアリスと申します」と、アリスはとてもていねいに答えました。でも、みんなしょせんトランプだと思うと、おびえる必要はないと思いました。

「して、この者どもは？」と、女王陛下は、バラの木のまわりではいつくばっている3人の庭師を指して言いました。顔を地面につけていたので、誰だかわからなかったのです。トランプの裏の模様は、みんな同じですから。

「なぜわたしが答えを知っているとお思いになるのですか？」と、強気になったアリスは質問しました。
　女王陛下は怒りで真っ赤になり、叫びました。「こやつの首をはねよ！こやつの首――」
　「正気で言ってるの！」と、アリスは大声で、きっぱりと言いました。女王陛下は黙ってしまいました。
　国王は女王陛下の腕に手を置き、さとしました。「ねえ、おまえ。まだ子どもなんだから！」　女王陛下は怒ってそっぽを向き、庭師たちに起き上がるよう命令しました。3人の庭師は、たちまち飛び起きて、王様、女王陛下、王家の子供たちやその他全員に、ぺこぺことお辞儀を始めました。
　「やめよ！」と女王陛下はわめきました。そして、3人がここで何をしていたのかを尋ねました。

"We were trying…" said Two.

"*I see!*" said the Queen, who had been looking at the roses. "Off with their heads!" and then she and everybody with her started walking on again. However, three of the guards stayed behind to kill the gardeners. The gardeners ran towards Alice so that she would look after them. They stood behind her so that they could not be seen.

The three guards walked round for a minute or two looking for the playing cards, and then they started walking after the others.

"Are their heads off?" cried the Queen.

"Their heads are gone," the guards shouted in reply.

The Queen then shouted, "Can you play croquet?"

The guards were silent and everyone looked at Alice because they thought the Queen must be asking her the question.

"Yes!" shouted Alice.

"Come on then!" cried the Queen, and Alice joined them wondering what would happen next.

"It's a very fine day!" said a quiet voice at her side. She was walking by the White Rabbit, who was looking worriedly into her face.

"Yes," said Alice. "Where's the Duchess?"

"Be quiet!" said the Rabbit. Then he said quietly to Alice, "The Queen has ordered the executioner to cut off the Duchess' head."

"Why?" asked Alice.

■ I see. 分かりました。　■ stay behind あとに残る　■ executioner 図 死刑執行人

「わたしどもは、何とかして……」と、2番は言いました。

「わかった!」と、バラを調べていた女王陛下は言いました。「この者たちの首をはねよ!」 そして、女王陛下始め、全員が、再び行進を続けました。3人の護衛兵は、庭師の刑を執行するために、残りました。庭師たちは助けを求めてアリスのそばに駆けより、アリスのうしろに身を隠しました。

3人の護衛兵は、1、2分歩き回ってトランプのカードたちを探しましたが、また行列を追って行進していきました。

「首をはねたか?」女王陛下は大声でわめきました。

「首は消え失せましてございます」と、護衛兵たちは大声で答えました。

「そなたはクロッケーができるか?」 女王陛下は続けて大声で言いました。

護衛兵たちは、みんな黙ってアリスの方を見ました。質問はあきらかに、アリスに向けられていると思ったからです。

「できます!」と、アリスは声をはりあげました。

「では、さあ、おいで!」 女王陛下は叫びました。アリスは行列について行きましたが、次にいったいどうなってしまうのかなあと考えました。

「とてもお天気がいいですね!」と言う声が、アリスのそばから聞こえてきました。アリスは、白ウサギのすぐ隣を歩いていたのです。白ウサギは不安げに、アリスの顔をのぞきこんでいます。

「ええ、ほんとうにね」と、アリスは答えました。「公爵夫人はどちら?」

「しーってば!」 白ウサギはアリスにささやきました。「あの方は、女王陛下から死刑の宣告をうけたんですよ」

「なんでまた?」とアリス。

"She hit the Queen's ears…" the Rabbit said. Alice laughed, but the Rabbit told her to stop. "The Queen will hear you! You see the Duchess came late and the Queen said…"

"Go to your places!" shouted the Queen in a very loud voice, and people began running about everywhere: however, in a minute or two the game began.

Alice thought that she had never seen such a strange croquet ground in all her life. It was very hilly; and the croquet balls were live hedgehogs (an animal) and the mallets were live flamingoes (a kind of bird), and the guards had to stand on their hands and feet to make the arches.

The main problem Alice had was holding her flamingo: She finally got its body safely under her arm, with its legs hanging down, but generally, just as she had got its head ready to hit the hedgehog, it *would* start moving round and would look up at her face in such a strange way that she could not do anything but laugh. And when she had got its head down and was ready to try again she could see that the hedgehog had moved away. Besides all this, the soldiers were always getting up and walking off to other parts of the ground, so Alice soon decided that it was a very difficult game to play.

■ hilly 形 起伏のある ■ live 形 生きている ■ hedgehog 名 ハリネズミ ■ mallet 名 打球づち ■ flamingo 名 フラミンゴ ■ arch 名 アーチ、弓形 ■ generally 副 大抵 ■ move away 立ち去る ■ walk off 立ち去る

Chapter VIII

「あの方は、女王陛下の両耳をひっぱたいてしまったんですよ……」と、ウサギは言いました。アリスはおかしくて、思わず吹き出してしまいましたが、すぐにウサギに止められてしまいました。「女王陛下に聞こえてしまうじゃないですか！　実は、公爵夫人は遅刻してしまって、女王陛下がおっしゃったことは……」

「位置に着け！」女王陛下が大声をあげたので、みんな、てんでんばらばらに走り出しました。でも、1、2分すると、ゲームが開始しました。

アリスにとって、生まれてこのかた、こんなヘンテコなクロッケー競技場は見たことがありませんでした。地面はでこぼこで、クロッケーのボールは生きたハリネズミ（動物）でした。ボールを打つクラブは、生きたフラミンゴ（鳥の一種）です。ボールをくぐらせるアーチは、護衛兵たちがからだを弓なりにまげ、手と足を地面につけているのです。

何より困ったのは、フラミンゴの持ち方でした。やっとのことで、アリスは、フラミンゴの胴体を小脇にかかえこみ、脚はだらりとたらすところまでできるようになりました。でも、首をまっすぐ伸ばさせ、その頭でハリネズミをコツンとやろうとすると、きまってフラミンゴは、ひょいっと首をねじってアリスの顔をのぞき込むのです。けげんな顔つきでアリスの顔をじっと見つめるので、アリスは思わず吹き出さずにはいられませんでした。それに、いざフラミンゴに頭を下げさせてもう一度やり直そうとしても、今度はハリネズミがちょこまか出て行ってしまうという具合です。それだけではなく、兵隊たちときたら、しょっちゅう起き上がって、競技場の他の場所にすたすた歩いていってしまうのです。とうとうアリスは、これはきわめて難解な試合だという結論に達しました。

The players all played at the same time, and talked angrily to each other, and in a very short time the Queen was very, very angry again and went round shouting "Off with his head!" or "Off with her head!"

Alice began to feel very worried: She had not yet had any problems with the Queen, but she knew that it might happen any minute, and so she was worried that she might also be killed.

"They really like killing people here," she thought, "it's surprising that anyone is still alive."

She was looking for a way to escape and wondering whether she could run away without being seen, but she noticed something strange. After watching it for a minute or two, she realised it was a grin and so she said to herself, "It's the Cheshire-Cat; now I shall have somebody to talk to."

"How are you getting on?" said the Cat.

When she could see all of the Cat, she put down her flamingo and told the Cat about the game, feeling very glad that she had someone to talk to. She told him everything that had happened and the problems she had had when the hedgehogs ran away.

"Do you like the Queen?" asked the Cat in a low voice.

"Not at all," said Alice, "she's so very…"

Just then she noticed that the Queen was near her, listening—so she continued, "…certain to win that there is no reason to finish the game." The Queen smiled and walked on.

■ in a short time 間もなく　■ any minute いつ何時　■ get on うまくいく　■ not at all とんでもない

Chapter VIII

　競技者はみな、同時にプレイをしており、ひっきりなしに口げんかをしています。たちまち女王陛下は癇癪(かんしゃく)をおこし、あちこち歩きまわりながら、「この男の首をはねよ！」だの、「この女の首をはねよ！」と声をはりあげるしまつです。

　アリスはだんだん落ち着かない気分になってきました。今のところ、女王陛下との間でとくに問題は起こっていませんが、いつそうなるかわかりません。そうしたら、自分の命も危ないと思いました。

　「ここの連中ときたら、首をはねるのが大好きだから」と、アリスは思いました。「まだ生きている人がいるのが不思議なくらいだわ」

　アリスはあたりを見わたして、逃げ道を探しました。誰にも気づかれずにいなくなる方法はないか、考えました。でもそこで、奇妙な存在に気がつきました。1、2分見つめていると、それはあの、ニヤニヤ笑いだということがわかりました。そこでアリスはつぶやきました。「チェシャーネコだわ。これで話し相手ができる」

　「やあ、調子はどうだい？」と、ネコは尋ねました。

　ネコの姿がまるごと現れたとき、アリスはフラミンゴを下におろして、ゲームのことを話し始めました。話を聞いてくれる相手がいることが、とてもうれしかったのです。アリスはネコに、起こったことをすべて話しました。そして、ハリネズミが走って逃げていってしまい、大変だったことも話しました。

　「女王陛下が好きかね？」と、ネコは声をひそめて聞きました。

　「ぜんぜん」と、アリスは言いました。「だって、あの人、あまりにも……」

　ちょうどそのとき、アリスのすぐそばに女王陛下が来て、聞き耳を立てているのに気づきました。そこでアリスは続けました。「……おじょうずだから、間違いなく優勝されるに決まっているもの。試合を最後までやる意味がないぐらいだわ」　女王陛下はにっこり笑って、立ち去りました。

"Who *are* you talking to?" asked the King, coming up to Alice and looking at the Cat.

"It's a friend of mine—a Cheshire-Cat," said Alice, "allow me to introduce it."

"I don't like the look of it at all," said the King, "however, it can kiss my hand."

"I'm sorry, I do not want to," the Cat said.

"Don't be so impolite," said the King, "and don't look at me like that!" He stood behind Alice as he spoke.

"A Cat may look at a King," said Alice. "I've read that in a book, but I don't remember which one."

"Well, we must change that," said the King; and he called to the Queen, who was passing at that moment, "My dear! I wish you would tell someone to take this Cat away!"

The Queen only had one answer. "Off with his head!" she said without even looking round.

"I'll go and get the executioner myself," said the King, and he hurried off. Alice decided to go back and see how the croquet game was going on, because she had heard the Queen's voice in the distance, shouting very loudly. She had already heard the Queen tell three of the players that their heads must be cut off by the executioner.

Alice could not understand what everyone was doing in the game, so she went off to look for her hedgehog.

■ come up to ～にやって来る　■ may 助 ～することができる《許可》　■ go off to ～に出掛ける

Chapter VIII

「誰に向かって話しておるのじゃ？」王様がアリスのそばに来て、ネコの顔をうさんくさそうに眺めて言いました。

「わたしのお友だちの、チェシャーネコさんです」とアリス。「紹介させてくださいな」

「この顔は、まったく気に食わんな」と、王様。「だが、この手に接吻を許してつかわすぞ」

「せっかくですが、お断りします」と、ネコは答えました。

「無礼者め」と、王様は言いました。「それに、そんな目つきでわしを見るな！」 そう言いながら王様は、アリスのうしろに隠れてしまいました。

「ネコにも王様を見る権利あり」 アリスは言いました。「って、いつか本で読んだことがあります。でも本の名前を思い出せません」

「うむ。それは変えなくてはいかんな」と、王様。そして、ちょうどそばを通りかかった女王陛下を呼びとめました。「のう、おまえ！　このネコをよそへやってくれんかな！」

女王陛下の答えは一つでした。「そやつの首をはねよ！」 女王陛下は見向きもせずに言いました。

「このわし自ら、処刑人を連れてまいろう」と言って、王様は急いで立ち去りました。アリスはクロッケーの試合がどうなったのか気になったので、見にもどることにしました。女王陛下のどなり声は、遠くからでも聞こえてきます。アリスは、すでに3人の選手の首をはねるよう、女王陛下が処刑人に命令しているのを聞いていました。

アリスは、みんなが競技場で何をしているのかわからなかったので、まずはとにかく、自分のハリネズミを探しに行くことにしました。

Her hedgehog was fighting with another hedgehog, which seemed to Alice a wonderful chance for her to hit one of them with the other: The only problem was that her flamingo had gone across to the other side of the garden and Alice could see it trying to fly up into a tree.

By the time she had caught the flamingo and brought it back the fight was over, and both the hedgehogs had gone away: "But it doesn't matter much," thought Alice, "because the soldiers who are making the arches have left this side of the ground." So she put the flamingo under her arm so that it would not escape again and went back to have a conversation with her friend the Cat.

When she got back to the Cheshire-Cat she was surprised to find a large number of people round it. The executioner, the King, and the Queen were having a conversation that sounded like a fight. They were all talking at the same time and everyone else was silent and looked very worried.

The moment Alice appeared, they all started talking to her and told her what they were talking about. They were all speaking at the same time so she found it very difficult to understand what they were saying.

■ fight with ～とけんかする ■ one of them with the other 一方で他方を ■ go across 横断する、渡る ■ fly up 飛び上がる ■ by the time ～する時までに ■ put ～ under one's arm ～を小脇に抱える ■ a large number of 大勢の

Chapter VIII

　アリスのハリネズミは、別のハリネズミとケンカの真っ最中でした。アリスは、自分のハリネズミを、もう一匹にぶつける、絶好のチャンスだと思いました。唯一の問題は、アリスのフラミンゴが、お庭の反対側に逃げて行ってしまったことでした。フラミンゴは木に飛び上がろうとしていました。

　アリスがフラミンゴを捕まえたころには、ハリネズミのケンカは終わっていて、2匹ともいなくなっていました。「まあ、別に構わないわ」と、アリスはつぶやきました。「だって、アーチを作っていた兵隊さんたちも、競技場のこっち側からみんないなくなってしまったんですもの」 そこでアリスは、逃げられないよう、がっちりとフラミンゴを小脇に抱え、さっきの友だちのネコのところにもどりました。また一緒におしゃべりがしたかったからです。

　アリスがチェシャーネコのところにもどってみると、驚いたことに、ネコのまわりには大勢の人だかり。どうやら処刑人と王様と女王陛下との間で、なにやら議論がくりひろげられているようでした。3人とも同時にまくしたてており、他の人たちはみんな、黙ったまま、不安げに見守っていました。

　アリスが現れるやいなや、3人はいっせいに、アリスに話し始めました。これまでみんなで話していたことも、ぜんぶアリスに伝えました。全員、いっぺんにまくしたてるものですから、何を言っているのか、聞き分けるだけでも大変でした。

The executioner was saying that he could not cut a head off unless there was a body to cut it off from: and that he had never done anything like that in his life so he did not want to do it then. The King was saying that anything that had a head could have its head cut off. The Queen was saying that if something was not done very quickly she would order the executioner to cut off everybody's heads.

Alice could think of nothing else to say, but she did say, "The Cheshire-Cat belongs to the Duchess, so you should ask *her* about it."

"She is in prison," said the Queen to the executioner. And then she told him to go and get the Duchess, so he did.

The Cat's head began disappearing the moment he had gone, and, by the time the executioner had come back with the Duchess, the Cat had completely disappeared: So the King and the executioner ran up and down looking for it, while the rest of the group went back to the croquet game.

■ unless 接 〜でない限り　■ prison 名 牢屋　■ run up and down 駆け足で上り下りする

処刑人の言い分は、胴体がないので、首をはねるのは無理な相談。それに、今までそんなことはやったことがないので、いまさらそんなお役はまっぴらごめん。王様の言い分は、頭がついているものはなんだって、首をはねられるはず。女王陛下といったら、ただちにことを起こさなければ、ここにいる全員の首を切り落とすよう処刑人に命じると、わめいています。

　アリスは言葉を失ってしまいました。でも、これだけは言いました。「チェシャーネコは、公爵夫人の飼いネコですから、公爵夫人に聞くべきだと思います」
　「あやつは牢屋に入っている」と、女王陛下は処刑人に言いました。そして、公爵夫人を連れてまいれと命令しました。
　処刑人が立ち去るやいなや、ネコの頭はすうっーとぼやけ始めました。そして、処刑人が公爵夫人を連れてもどってきたころには、ネコの姿はあとかたもなく消えていました。王様と処刑人は、やっきになってあちこち探しまわりましたが、他の人たちはみな、ぞろぞろとクロッケーの試合にもどって行きました。

覚えておきたい英語表現

> "Who are you?"（p.72, 4行目）
> 「君はいったい何者だね？」

【解説】イモムシは、"Who are you?" と切り出しました。「あんた誰？」というニュアンスにも受け取れます。言い方によっては、初対面の相手に対して失礼に聞こえます。カジュアルに尋ねるのなら、"What is your name?"「名前を教えてくれる？」

礼儀をわきまえるのなら、自分の名前を名乗ってから相手の名前を聞きます。

"I am Mr. Caterpillar. May I ask your name, young lady?"
「わたしの名前はMr.イモムシです。お嬢さん、お名前を尋ねてもいいですか？」

笑顔で尋ねたら、コミュニケーションが成り立ちます。不思議の国のアリスの登場人物たちは、なぜか、心地よいコミュニケーションをアリスと展開してくれません。

【例文】① Who do you think you are?
自分のことをいったい何さまだと思っているんだ？

＊礼儀知らずの相手に対して使える表現です。

② Who are you, if I may ask?
よろしければ、どなたなのか、教えていただけません？

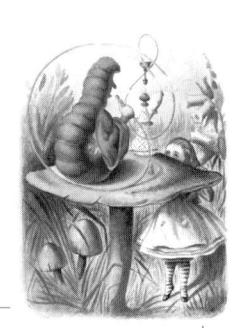

> The Caterpillar seemed to be very unkind. （p.74, 15行目）
> イモムシはすごく不親切に思えました。

【解説】mean（いじわる）の代わりに、unkind（不親切）という言葉が使われています。やさしくて賢明なアリスは、ネガティブなことを言うとき、ポジティブな言葉を土台にして、un- で否定しています。

$$\underset{(非・不)}{\text{un}} \text{ または } \underset{(ではない)}{\text{not}} + \underset{(親切・やさしい)}{\text{kind}} = \text{やさしくない}$$

となります。uncool（クールじゃない・ダサい）も、よく使われる"クール"な表現です。日常会話でも、ビジネスでも、言いにくいことを言うときには、否定的な言葉を使うよりも、この方法でコミュニケーションを進めていくと、よりスムーズに難局を乗り越えることができます。

♥2♥

【例文】①The weather has not been very kind to us lately.
　　　　ここのところ、お天気はご機嫌ななめですね。

　　　②Bullying is so UNcool!
　　　　いじめはサイテー！

"You'll get used to it soon,"（p.82, 11行目）
「すぐに慣れるよ」

【解説】get used to 〜 は、「〜に慣れる」という意味です。慣れることは、新しい環境に順応することでもあり、サバイバルのコツです。
　突然、8センチに満たないほど縮んでしまいショックを受けているアリスに対して、同じぐらい小さなイモムシはつぶやきます。たしかに、大きさも、美しさも、富も、この世の中の何もかも、Everything is relative.（すべて相対的）ですよね。多くの人たちは、何かと比較して、大きいとか小さいとか、きれいとか、きれいじゃないとかを、判断しているのです。

【例文】①Try to get used to the new food, and enjoy it!
　　　　初めての食べ物に早く慣れて、エンジョイしなさい！

　　　②Once you get used to the culture here, you'll come to like it.
　　　　ここの文化に慣れたら、きっと気に入るよ。

"It makes a lot of difference to me,"（p.88, 18行目）
「わたしには大違いよ」

【解説】make a difference（違い・変化を起こす）は、非常によく使われる表現です。ポジティブな変化や変革を、自分自身や社会にもたらすという意味でも用いられます。

【例文】①You can make a difference in the world with your passion!
　　　　君の情熱で、世界を変えることができる！

149

覚えておきたい英語表現

②She is making a wonderful difference in people who come in touch with her.
　彼女と触れ合う人はみな、素晴らしい変身を遂げる。

> "'Time' is 'him' not 'it'!" said the Hatter.　(p.116, 23行目)
> 「時間は"彼"で、"それ"ではない！」と、帽子屋。

【解説】Hatter（帽子屋）は、March Hare同様、'as mad as a hatter (or a March hare)' の英語表現に端を発しています。帽子職人はしばしば発狂し、繁殖期の三月ウサギは狂ったように飛び跳ねるという言い伝えから生まれた、「頭の変な」という意味の成句です。

　帽子屋は、Time（時間）を、大文字で始まる固有名詞として擬人化しています。それを受ける代名詞は、it（それ）ではなく、him（彼）となります。従って、"時間クン"は、"人並み"の扱いが必要になるのです。

【例文】①Give it time.
　　　　時間をかけよ。

　　　②Only time cures…
　　　　時間だけが、心の痛みを癒してくれる……

　　　　＊私たちも、"時間クン"を大いに味方にして、
　　　　一瞬一瞬を大切に生きましょう！

> "I haven't had any tea," Alice replied, "so I can't take any more."　(p.124, 5行目)
> 「わたし、まだお茶をいただいていないんですけど」と、アリスは答えました。「だからお代りはできません」

【解説】"Take some more tea." 「お茶のお代わりはいかが？」と、三月ウサギに勧められ、アリスが返答します。

　someは、はっきりと数や量を示さなくても、そこに"存る"ことを示す単語です。some more は、すでに飲んでいるお茶がまだそこに"在り"、"もっと"いかがですか？と勧める表現です。

アリスは、haven't had any tea（そもそもまだお茶をいただいていないので）、can't take any more（これ以上飲むわけにいかない——お代りは不可能）と言っています。more（もっと）を使った、言葉遊びです。

【例文】① Have you had any sleep?
　　　　　少しは寝たの？

　　　　② No, I don't need any more sleep. I slept 12 hours yesterday.
　　　　　いや、これ以上睡眠時間は必要ないよ。だって昨日、12時間寝たからね。

"Their heads are gone."（p.136, 11行目）
「首は消え失せましてございます」

【解説】女王陛下の質問、"Are their heads off?"「首ははねたか？」に対して、YesかNoとは言わず、護衛兵たちは別の答え方をしています。

　headsとは、頭を指しますが、頭で代表される身体全体も指します。head countは、人員数を意味します。Their headsという表現で、首（頭）がついた身体全体にすり替えられていることに気づかない女王陛下は、期待通り、「首」がはねられたと解釈して満足します。このからくりは、metonymy（換喩法）と呼びます。赤ずきんちゃんのことを、Red Riding Hood（赤ずきん）と言うのと同じです。

　また、goneには、「去った・消えた」のほかに、「亡くなった」という意味があります。護衛兵たちは、「首ごとどこかへ消えていってしまった」と言い、ウソはついていません。女王陛下のはやとちりは、私たちの日常のコミュニケーションにおいても頻繁に起こっています。人の話をじっくりと聞くように心がけましょう。

【例文】① Stay with us, Grandpa!
　　　　　「おじいちゃん、逝かないで！」

　　　　He's gone…
　　　　　「もう逝ってしまった……」

　　　　＊直接的な言葉を使わず、stay（現世に留まる）と、gone（あの世に旅立った）という表現を使います。

　　　　② Two heads are better than one.
　　　　　「三人寄れば文殊の知恵」

　　　　＊日本語では三人ですが、英語では、「二つの頭をつきあわせれば、一つの頭で考えるよりも、良い知恵が生まれる」という表現になります。

覚えておきたい英語表現

"It's the Cheshire-Cat; now I shall have somebody to talk to."
（p.140, 12行目）
「チェシャーネコだわ。これで話し相手ができる」

【解説】チェシャーは、イングランド中西部の州で、著者ルイス・キャロルの生誕地です。でも、チェシャーネコという種類のネコはないそうです。

18世紀、チェシャー産の黄白色の固いチェシャー ＝ チーズには、ニヤッと笑ったネコのマークがついていたという説があります。to grin like a Cheshire cat.（チェシャーネコのようにニヤッと笑う）という成句から抜け出したチェシャーネコは、体が消えても、空にはニヤニヤ笑いが残るという仕掛けになっています。

have somebody to talk to（話し相手ができる）は、首をはねるのが大好きな女王陛下から逃れたくなったアリスにとって、ホッとする瞬間でした。somebody（誰か）は、人間でも動物でも、話しかける相手であれば誰でもよいので、この単語を使っています。talk to は、"語る"ことです。話し合って、相手と心を通わせることをも意味します。一方 speak to は、状況によっては、"一方的にしゃべる" という印象を与えることもあります。

listenとhearの間にも、"聞き方"の姿勢に違いがあります。hearは、ただ聞く、聞き流すときにも使います。一方 listen は、相手を理解するために、耳を傾けることを指します。

【例文】① Stop speaking and TALK to me!
　　　　おしゃべりはやめて、僕と向き合って話してくれ。

　　　② I hear you. But, I don't want to listen to you any more.
　　　　あなたの声は聞こえてるけど、あなたの話はもう聞きたくないの。

Part 3
Chapter IX-XII

Chapter IX
The Mock Turtle's Story *p. 154*
海ガメもどきの話

Chapter X
The Lobster-Quadrille *p. 170*
ロブスターのカドリールダンス

Chapter XI
Who Stole the Tarts? *p. 190*
タルト泥棒は誰？

Chapter XII
Alice's Evidence *p. 206*
アリスの証言

Chapter IX

The Mock Turtle's Story

"I am very glad to see you again, you dear old thing!" said the Duchess, as she put her arm into Alice's, and they walked off together.

Alice was very glad to find her so friendly, and she thought to herself that perhaps it was only the pepper that had made her so angry when they met in the kitchen.

"When *I'm* a Duchess," she said to herself (not in a very hopeful way though), "I won't have any pepper in my kitchen *at all*. Soup is delicious without it. Maybe it is always pepper that makes people angry," she continued, very pleased at thinking of this new idea.

She had forgotten the Duchess by this time and was a little surprised when she heard her voice close to her ear. "You're thinking about something, my dear, and that makes you forget to talk. I can't tell you just now why that is impolite, but I will remember it in a moment.

■ mock 形 偽物の、見せかけの　■ old thing 旧友
■ hopeful 形 望みを抱いている

第 9 章
海ガメもどきの話

「まあ、あなた！またお会いできてほんとうにうれしいこと！」と、公爵夫人は、アリスの腕に自分の腕をからめ、一緒に歩きながら言いました。

公爵夫人がこんなに親しげなので、アリスはとてもうれしく思いました。夫人の台所で会ったとき夫人がすごくおかんむりだったのは、きっとコショウのせいに違いないと思いました。

「もしわたしが公爵夫人だったら」と、アリスはひとりごとを言いました（すごくなりたいと思っている感じではなく）。「台所には絶対に、コショウを置かないことにするわ。スープだってコショウを入れなくてもおいしいし。人がぴりぴりしてしまうのは、いつだってコショウのせいかもしれないわ」と、この新しい思いつきに満足しながら、アリスはひとりごとを続けました。

アリスはいつのまにやら、公爵夫人のことをすっかり忘れてしまっていました。夫人がアリスの耳もとでささやいたときには、ちょっとびっくりしました。「ねえ、お嬢ちゃん、あなた、なにか考えごとをしているわね。だからおしゃべりを忘れてしまうのよね。それがどうしてお行儀が悪いことなのか、今すぐには言えないけど、すぐに思い出すわね」

"Perhaps it isn't," said Alice.

"Now, now child!" said the Duchess. "There is a reason for everything if you can think of it." And she moved herself closer to Alice as she spoke.

Alice did not like the Duchess standing too close to her; firstly, because she was able to rest her head on Alice's shoulder, and secondly, because her head was a very hard one. However, she did not like to be impolite, so she stayed quiet.

"The game has become much better," she said, trying to think of something to say.

"Yes, it has," said the Duchess. And then she added, "I am sure you are wondering why I don't put my arm round you. Well, the reason is that I'm doubtful about the feelings of your flamingo. Shall I try?"

"He might bite you," Alice replied, not wanting the Duchess to try this.

"Very true," said the Duchess.

There was silence for a bit, and then the Duchess asked, "Thinking again?" and rested her head even more on Alice's shoulder.

"I can think if I want to," said Alice quickly because she was beginning to feel a little worried.

But suddenly, to Alice's great surprise, the Duchess started shaking, and the arm that was round Alice's shoulders went away. Alice looked up and saw the Queen standing in front of them looking very, very angry.

■ rest 動 〜を置く　■ doubtful 形 疑わしい　■ bite 動 かみつく

Chapter IX

「もしかしたら、お行儀が悪いことではないかもしれません」と、アリス。

「ねえ、ちょっと待って、お嬢ちゃん！」と、公爵夫人。「考えさえしたら、どんなことだって、ちゃんと理由があるものよ」　そう話しながら、夫人はますますアリスの近くにすり寄ってきます。

アリスは、公爵夫人にこんなにぴったりとくっつかれるのはあまり好きではありませんでした。だって夫人ときたら、頭をアリスの肩にどかっとのせることができたし、その頭はものすごく固かったからです。でも、アリスは礼儀正しくしておこうと思い、何も言いませんでした。

「クロッケーの試合は、かなりよくなってきましたね」　アリスは会話をもたせようと気遣って言いました。

「たしかに」と、公爵夫人は言ったあと、続けました。「わたしがどうして腕をあなたの腰にまわさないのか、不思議に思っているでしょう。それはねえ、あなたのフラミンゴの御機嫌が気にかかるからなのよ、ためしてみましょうか？」

「かみつかれるかもしれませんよ」と、アリスは答えました。公爵夫人にためしてほしくなかったからです。

「たしかに」と、公爵夫人。

しばらく間があいたあと、夫人は尋ねました。「また考えごと中？」と言って、頭をアリスの肩にどっかりとのせてきます。

「わたしだって、考えようと思ったら、考えられます」と、アリスはあわてて言いました。ちょっと不安になってきたからです。

その瞬間、アリスがびっくりしたことに、公爵夫人がぶるぶると震えだしたのです。アリスの肩にまわしていた腕もひっこめました。見上げると、仁王立ちになった女王陛下が二人の前に立っていました。

"It's a lovely day, isn't it!" the Duchess began in a low, quiet voice.

"I am telling you now," shouted the Queen hitting her feet on the ground as she spoke, "either you leave now, or your head will be cut off! Take your choice!" The Duchess took her choice and left in a moment.

"Let's continue with the game," the Queen said to Alice; and Alice was too afraid to say a word, but slowly she followed her back to the croquet ground.

The other guests were resting, but, as soon as they saw the Queen again, they hurried back to the game. The Queen, however, had seen them, and she told them their heads would be cut off if they rested again.

All the time they were playing, the Queen never stopped fighting with the other players or shouting "Off with his head!" or "Off with her head!" Those whom she sent to the executioner were taken away by the soldiers (who, of course, had to stop being arches to do this) so that, after half an hour or so, there were no arches left and all the players, except the King, the Queen, and Alice, had been taken away.

Then the Queen stopped because she felt very tired, and she said to Alice, "Have you seen the Mock Turtle yet?"

"No," said Alice. "I don't even know what a Mock Turtle is."

"It's the thing Mock Turtle soup is made from," said the Queen.

"I've never seen one or even heard of one," said Alice.

"Come on then," said the Queen, "and he will tell you his story."

■ either A or B AかそれともB　■ take one's choice 好きなものを取る　■ those whom ～する人々　■ be taken away 連れて行かれる　■ be made from （原料）でできている

Chapter IX

「けっこうなお日和でございますね！」と、公爵夫人は、消え入るような声であいさつしました。

「よいか、よく聞け」と、女王陛下は足をふみならしながら言いました。「おまえがいなくなるか、おまえの首が飛ぶかだ！さっさと選ぶのじゃ！」 公爵夫人はすぐに選択して、あっという間に消えてしまいました。

「それではゲームを続けるとするか」と、女王陛下はアリスに向かって言いました。アリスはおびえて言葉が出ませんでした。でも、女王陛下について、クロッケー場へとのろのろともどって行きました。

ほかのお客たちは、休憩中でした。でも、女王陛下の姿が見えたとたん、みんな大急ぎでゲームにもどりました。女王陛下は、彼らが休憩しているのを見ていたので、もしまた休憩したら、今度は首が飛ぶぞ！　と警告しました。

競技中、女王陛下はひっきりなしに他の選手とケンカをしていました。または、「こやつの首をはねよ！」とか、「この女の首をはねよ！」と叫んでいました。宣告を下された者は、兵隊たちに連れ出されました（そうするためには当然、兵隊たちはアーチをやめなければなりませんでした）。そういうわけで、30分もすると、アーチは全部なくなってしまい、王様と女王陛下とアリスをのぞいた全員が、連行されてしまいました。

女王陛下はそこで試合をやめました。ずいぶんとくたびれてしまったのです。「海ガメもどきとはもう会ったかい？」と、アリスに尋ねました。

「いいえ」と、アリス。「海ガメもどきって、何のことなのかもわかりません」

「海ガメもどきスープの材料だよ」と、女王陛下。

「そんなの見たことも聞いたこともありません」と、アリス。

「さあ、もっと近う寄れ」と、女王陛下は言いました。「こやつに身の上話をさせてやろう」

As they walked off together, Alice heard the King say to everyone, in a low voice, "You are all excused."

"*That's* a good thing," Alice said to herself, because she had felt quite unhappy at the number of people the Queen had sent to the Executioner.

Very soon they saw a Gryphon lying asleep in the sun.

"Get up!" said the Queen, "and take this young lady to see the Mock Turtle and to hear his history. I must go back and see if the Executioner is doing his job." She walked off, leaving Alice alone with the Gryphon. Alice did not like the look of the animal, but she thought it would be as safe to stay with it as it would be to follow the Queen, so she waited.

The Gryphon sat up and washed his eyes, then it watched the Queen until she could not be seen. Then it laughed. "What fun," said the Gryphon.

"What do you *mean*?" asked Alice.

"I mean *her*," said the Gryphon. "She believes that they cut off people's heads but nobody does, you know. Come on!"

■ excuse 動 許す　■ gryphon 名 グリフォン《ギリシア神話に登場する鷲の頭と翼を持ち胴体がライオンの怪物》　■ sit up 起き上がる、きちんと座る

Chapter IX

　二人が連れだって立ち去るとき、アリスには、王様が声をひそめて一同にこう言っているのが聞こえました。「全員釈放じゃ」
　「ほんとうによかった！」と、アリスはつぶやきました。女王陛下が言い渡した死刑宣告のあまりの多さに、すっかり気がめいっていたのです。
　ほどなく、日向ぼっこをしてすやすやと眠っているグリフォン（ギリシャ神話に登場する怪獣）のところにやってきました。
　「起きよ！」と、女王陛下は命令しました。「このお嬢さんを海ガメもどきのところへご案内し、やつの話を聞かせてやるのじゃ。わらわはもどって、命じておいた処刑を見とどけねばならぬ」　女王陛下は、アリスをグリフォンと二人きりにして、立ち去ってしまいました。アリスは、この生きものは、見た感じ、あまり好みではありませんでした。でも、女王陛下についていくのも、グリフォンと一緒にいるのも、安全面ではさして変わらないと思えたのでここで待つことにしました。
　グリフォンは起き上がって、目をこすって洗い、女王陛下が見えなくなるまで見送りました。それから、くっくっと笑い、「おかしいよな」と言いました。
　「なにが？」と、アリスは尋ねました。
　「なにって、あの女だよ」と、グリフォンは言いました。「首を切り落とすつもりになっているだけなんだよ。でも実際には、だれ一人処刑なんかしていないんだ。わかるだろう。さあおいで！」

"Everybody says 'come on' here," thought Alice, as she walked slowly after the Gryphon: "I've never been so ordered about before in all my life—never!"

They had only gone a short way when they saw the Mock Turtle in the distance, sitting sad and lonely on a small rock, and, as they came nearer, Alice could hear him making very sad noises, as if he was crying. She felt sorry for him. "Why is he sad?" she asked the Gryphon. And the Gryphon answered, very nearly in the same words as before, "He's not really sad, you know. Come on!"

So they went up to the Mock Turtle, who looked at them with large eyes full of tears but said nothing.

"This young lady," said the Gryphon, "wants to know your history."

"I'll tell it to her," said the Mock Turtle in a deep voice: "Sit down, both of you, and don't say a word until I have finished."

So they sat down and nobody spoke for some minutes. Alice thought to herself, "I don't see how he can *ever* finish, if he doesn't begin." But she waited patiently.

"Once," said the Mock Turtle at last, with a deep breath, "I was a real Turtle."

These words were followed by a very long silence, broken only by an occasional cry of "Hjckrrh!" from the Gryphon and the constant heavy crying of the Mock Turtle.

■ full of tears 涙でいっぱいにして　■ occasional 形 時折の　■ constant 形 絶えず続く

Chapter IX

「ここではみんな、『さあおいで』って言うのね」と、アリスはグリフォンのあとをとぼとぼついて行きながら思いました。「わたし、生まれてこのかた、こんなにたくさん命令されたことなんか一度もなかった、ほんとうに!」

ちょっと行くと、遠くに海ガメもどきの姿が見えてきました。小さな岩の上にひとりさびしくぽつんと座っていました。近づいていくと、まるですすり泣いているような悲しい声を出していました。アリスはかわいそうになって、「なぜあんなに悲しんでいるの?」と、グリフォンに尋ねました。するとグリフォンは、さっきとほとんど同じセリフで答えました。「ほんとはちっとも悲しくなんかないんだよ。わかるだろう。さあおいで!」

そしてふたりは、海ガメもどきのそばに近づきました。海ガメもどきは、大きな目にうるうると涙をためて、無言で二人を見つめました。

「こちらのお嬢ちゃんが」と、グリフォンは言いました。「おまえさんの身の上話を聞きたがってるよ」

「話して聞かせよう」と、海ガメもどきは、深く沈んだ声で言いました。「そこに座りなさい、ふたりとも。話が終わるまで、一言も口をはさんじゃいかんぞ」

ふたりは腰をおろし、数分間、誰も一言も言いませんでした。アリスは、「始めなければ、永遠にお話は終わらないのに」と思いましたが、しんぼう強く待つことにしました。

「昔は」と、海ガメもどきは深いため息をついたあと、重い口を開きました。「わしはほんものの海ガメだった」

この言葉のあと、長い長い沈黙が続きました。ときおりグリフォンが、「ヒュイックルル!」という叫び声をあげ、ひっきりなしにすすり泣く海ガメもどきの重くるしい泣き声が響きました。

Alice nearly got up and said, "Thank you, sir, for your interesting story," but she was sure there *must* be more of the story to come, so she sat still and said nothing.

"When we were little," the Mock Turtle added at last, more happily but still crying a little now and then, "we went to school in the sea. The teacher was an old Turtle—we used to call him 'Tortoise'…"

"Why did you call him Tortoise, if he wasn't one?" asked Alice.

"We called him Tortoise because we wanted to," said the Mock Turtle angrily. "Really, you are very uninteresting!"

"You should feel very bad for asking such an easy question," added the Gryphon, and then they sat silently and looked at poor Alice, who felt very stupid. At last the Gryphon said to the Mock Turtle, "Go on, old man! Don't take all day to tell us about it!" and he continued with these words—

"Yes, we went to school in the sea, though you probably don't believe it…"

"I never said that I didn't believe you!" shouted Alice.

"You did," said the Mock Turtle.

"Be quiet!" added the Gryphon before Alice could speak again. The Mock Turtle went on speaking.

■ sit still　じっと座っている　■ tortoise　图（陸生の）カメ《「トータス」は、taught us（ぼくらに教えてくれた）の言葉遊び》　■ feel stupid　ばかみたいな気がする

Chapter IX

　アリスは、「とても興味深いお話をありがとうございました」と言って立ち上がりそうになりましたが、きっとまだお話の続きがあるに違いないと思い、そのまま黙って座っていることにしました。

　「子どものころはな」と、海ガメもどきはとうとう先を続けてくれました。まだときどきすすり泣きながらも、さっきよりもちょっと明るい口調でした。「海の中にある学校に通っていたんだ。先生はおじいさん海ガメだったけど、先生のことをわしらは、『山ガメ先生』って呼んでいた」

　「どうして海ガメなのに山ガメって呼んでいたの？」と、アリスは聞いてみました。

　「ただそう呼びたかったからさ」と、海ガメもどきはぷりぷり怒って答えました。「まったくあんたは、つまらないやつだなあ！」

　「わかりきった質問をして、はずかしくないのかい」と、グリフォンも追い打ちをかけます。それから2匹は黙って座ったまま、わたしってなんておバカさんなんだろうと思って沈みこんでいるかわいそうなアリスをじっと見つめました。やがてグリフォンは海ガメもどきに、「ほら、じいさん。はやく続きを話してくれよ。日が暮れちまう！」と言ったので、海ガメもどきは次のように続けました。

　「そう、わしらは海の中にある学校に通っていたんだ。たぶん信じてくれないだろうがね……」

　「信じられないなんて、わたしそんなこと言った覚えはありません！」と、アリスは声をはりあげました。

　「言ったよ」と、海ガメもどき。

　「うるさい！」と、グリフォンが、アリスが言い返そうとする前に口をはさみました。海ガメもどきは、先を続けました。

"We had the best education—in fact, we went to school every day…"

"*I* go to school every day, too," said Alice. "Everybody goes to school every day so it is not unusual."

"And did you learn French and music?" asked the Mock Turtle, a little worriedly.

"Yes," said Alice: "we did."

"And washing?" asked the Mock Turtle.

"Certainly not!" said Alice.

"Ah! Then yours wasn't a really good school," said the Mock Turtle feeling very much happier. "Now, at our school, they had French, music, *and washing*—as well as the usual subjects."

"But why did you want to learn 'washing'?" asked Alice. "You were living at the bottom of the sea."

"I did not have enough money to learn washing," said the Mock Turtle sadly. "I could only take the general course."

"What was *that*?" asked Alice.

"Reading and writing, of course, to begin with," the Mock Turtle replied, "and then all the different kinds of mathematics, and uglification."

"I've never heard of 'uglification'," said Alice. "What is it?"

The Gryphon looked up in surprise. "Never heard of 'uglifying'!" it cried. "Do you know what 'to beautify' is?"

"Yes," said Alice, "it means to make something beautiful."

■ washing 图 洗濯　■ certainly not とんでもない　■ subject 图 科目、教科
■ general course 普通課程　■ mathematics 图 数学　■ uglification 图 醜態学
■ beautify 動 美化する

「わしらはな、最高の教育を受けておった。毎日欠かさず学校に行っていたのだ……」

「わたしだって、毎日学校に通っています」と、アリス。「だれだって毎日学校に通うものよ。それが普通でしょ」

「それならおまえさんは、フランス語や音楽を勉強したかい？」と、いささか不安そうに、海ガメもどきはアリスに尋ねました。

「ええ」と、アリスは答えました。「習いました」

「じゃあ洗濯は？」と、海ガメもどき。

「もちろん習ってません！」と、アリス。

「ほら言っただろう！　あんたの学校は、一流の学校じゃなかったんだって」と、うれしそうに海ガメもどき。「一方、わしらの学校ではな、フランス語も、音楽も、洗濯も、ほかの科目に加えて教えてくれたんじゃ」

「でもなんだって、"洗濯"なんか選択したかったのですか？」と、アリスは尋ねました。「だって海の底に暮らしていたんでしょ」

「金がなかったから、洗濯を選択することはできなかったんだ」と、海ガメもどきは悲しそうに言いました。「わしが習えたのは、普通科目だけだった」

「それはどんな科目？」と、アリス。

「まずは読み書き」と、海ガメもどきは答えました。「それに、いろいろな種類の数学と醜態学だ」

「醜態学なんて、初めて聞いたわ」と、アリス。「どんなお勉強なんですか？」

グリフォンはびっくりしてアリスの顔を見上げ、「"醜態学"を知らないなんて！」と、大声をあげました。「あんたは、『美化する』という言葉は知っているかい？」

「もちろんよ」と、アリス。「何かを美しくすることでしょ」

"Well then," the Gryphon continued, "if you don't know what to 'uglify' is, then you *are* very strange."

Alice did not want to ask any more questions about it so she turned to the Mock Turtle and asked him what else he had learned.

"Well, there was history," the Mock Turtle replied, "old and new, then drawing—the drawing teacher was a conger eel (a kind of fish) that used to come and teach us once a week."

"And how many hours a day did you have lessons?" said Alice.

"Ten hours the first day," said the Mock Turtle, "nine the next, and so on."

"What a strange plan!" cried Alice. This was a new idea for her and she thought about it before she asked her next question.

"Then the eleventh day must have been a holiday?" she asked.

"Of course it was," said the Mock Turtle.

"And what did you do on the twelfth day?" asked Alice.

"That's enough about lessons," said the Gryphon very firmly. "Tell her something about the games now."

■ conger eel アナゴ　■ and so on 〜など　■ firmly 副 きっぱりと

Chapter IX

「それなら」と、グリフォンは続けました。「『醜態化──醜くする』の意味がわからないなんて、ほんとうにあんたはヘンだな」

アリスはもうこれ以上、この話題に関する質問をしたくなかったので、海ガメもどきの方を向いて、他に学校で習ったことについて尋ねました。

「そうじゃな。歴史も習った」と、海ガメもどきは答えました。「古代と現代のだ。それに絵画の授業もあった。担任はアナゴ（魚の一種）先生で、週一回の授業だった」

「毎日、何時間ぐらい授業があったんですか？」と、アリス。

「1日目は10時間で」と、海ガメもどき。「2日目は9時間で、といった具合さ」

「へんてこりんな時間割ですね！」と、アリスは叫びました。でも、これはアリスにとって、まったく新鮮な考え方だったので、次の質問をする前に少し考えてから、こう尋ねました。

「ということは、11日目はお休みになりますね」

「もちろんじゃ」と、海ガメもどき。

「それじゃあ12日目はどうしたんですか？」と、アリスは聞きました。

「授業の話はもう十分」と、グリフォンはきっぱりと言いました。「次は、この子に遊びの話をしてやりな」

Chapter X

The Lobster-Quadrille

The Mock Turtle breathed deeply. He looked at Alice and tried to speak, but for a minute or two his cries stopped him speaking. The Gryphon started shaking him and hitting him, and it seemed to help. At last the Mock Turtle could speak again, and, with tears running down his face, he continued.

"You may not have lived much under the sea…"

"I haven't," said Alice.

"…perhaps you were never even introduced to a lobster…"

(Alice began to say "I once ate…" but she stopped herself quickly and said, "No never".)

"…so you can have no idea what a wonderful dance a Lobster-Quadrille is!"

"No, indeed," said Alice. "What sort of dance is it?"

"Why," said the Gryphon, "you must first make a line along the beach."

■ Quadrille カドリール《4組の男女のカップルがスクエア（四角）になって踊る歴史的ダンスで、伝統的スクエアダンスの先駆け》 ■ seem to 〜のように見える ■ stop oneself 思いとどまる ■ make a line 一列になる

第 10 章
ロブスターのカドリールダンス

　海ガメもどきは深いため息をつきました。アリスを見つめてなにか言おうとしましたが、1、2分泣きじゃくって声が出ません。グリフォンが海ガメもどきをゆさぶったり、たたいたりしたら、ようやく声が出るようになりました。涙が頬をつたい落ちるなか、海ガメもどきは再び先を続けました。

「海の底で暮らしたことはあまりないかもしれないが……」
「ないです」と、アリス。
「……ロブスターに紹介されたこともないようだな……」
(「一度食べ……」と言いかけましたが、はっとしてやめ、あわてて答えました。「一度もないです」)
「ということは、ロブスターのカドリールダンスの素晴らしさは想像できないだろうな！」
「ええ、ぜんぜん」と、アリス。「それって、どんな踊りなんですか？」
「それはね」とグリフォン。「まず海岸に沿って一列に並ぶ」

"Two lines!" cried the Mock Turtle.

"*That* generally takes some time," said the Gryphon. "Then you walk forward two steps…"

"Each with a lobster as a partner!" cried the Gryphon.

"Of course," the Mock Turtle said.

"Go forward two steps, change lobsters, and then go back in the same way," added the Gryphon.

"Then you know," the Mock Turtle continued, "you throw the…"

"The lobsters!" shouted the Gryphon.

"…as far out into the sea as you can."

"And then you swim after them!" shouted the Gryphon.

"You turn over and over in the sea!" cried the Mock Turtle, moving wildly about.

"Change lobsters again!" shouted the Gryphon.

"Then you come back to land again, and—that is all the first part of the game," said the Mock Turtle, suddenly making his voice much quieter; and the two animals who had been jumping about like mad things all this time sat down again very sadly and quietly and looked at Alice.

"It must be a pretty dance," said Alice quietly.

"Would you like to see a little of it?" asked the Mock Turtle.

"Yes, very much indeed," said Alice.

"Come, let us try the first part!" said the Mock Turtle to the Gryphon. "We can do it without lobsters, you know. Who will sing?"

■ take some time いくらか時間がかかる　■ walk forward 前に進む　■ in the same way 同様に　■ far out はるか向こうに　■ turn over and over 何度も繰り返して転がる　■ wildly 副 むやみやたらに、激しく　■ pretty 形 素敵な

「2列じゃよ！」と、海ガメもどき。
「これにはいつも時間がかかる」と、グリフォンは言いました。「次に2歩前へ進み……」
「ロブスターとペアになって！」と、グリフォンが叫びました。
「もちろんじゃ」と、海ガメもどき。
「また2歩進んで、チェンジ（ロブスター）パートナー。同じ順序でうしろに下がる」と、グリフォン。
「それからじゃったな」と、海ガメもどきは続けます。「投げるのじゃ……」
「ロブスターたちを！」と、グリフォンは大声で叫びました。
「……思いっきり沖のほうへ」
「それから、ロブスターたちを追いかけて泳ぐ！」と、グリフォンが絶叫。
「そして海の中で何度もとんぼ返りして！」と、海ガメもどきがわめいて、めちゃくちゃ飛び跳ねました。
「もう一度ロブスターを取っかえて！」と、グリフォンの金切り声。
「それから陸までもどって、そこで——ダンスの最初のところが終了」と、海ガメもどきが、急に声を落として言いました。そうして2匹は、ついさっきまで狂ったかのように跳ねまわっていたのに、妙に悲しげに黙りこくって座り、アリスを見つめました。

「とても素敵な踊りなんでしょうね」と、アリスはおずおずと言いました。
「ちょっとだけ見てみたいかね？」と、海ガメもどき。
「はい。ぜひお願いします」と、アリス。
「おいで。出だしのところをやってみよう！」と、海ガメもどきがグリフォンに言いました。「ロブスターたちなしでもできるじゃろ。だれが歌う？」

"Oh, *you* sing," said the Gryphon. "I've forgotten the words."

So they began dancing round and round Alice, every now and then stepping on her feet when they passed too close, while the Mock Turtle sang this song, very slowly and sadly—

"Will you walk a little faster?" said a whiting to a snail,
"There's a porpoise close behind us, and he's walking on my tail.
See how happily the lobsters and turtles all walk on!
They are waiting on the beach—will you come and join the dance?
 Will you, won't you, will you, won't you, will you join the
  dance?
 Will you, won't you, will you, won't you, will you join the
  dance?"

"You can really have no idea how wonderful it will be
When they take us up and throw us with the lobsters into the sea!"
But the snail replied, "Too far, too far!" and looked away.
He thanked the whiting kindly, but would not join the dance.
 Would not, could not, would not, could not,
  would not join the dance.
 Would not, could not, would not, could not,
  would not join the dance.

■ dance around 踊り回る　■ Will you ～してくださいませんか　■ whiting 名 ホワイティング《タラ科の魚》　■ snail 名 巻き貝　■ porpoise 名 ネズミイルカ　■ take up ～を持ち上げる、抱き上げる

「ああ、おまえさんが歌っておくれよ」とグリフォン。「おれは歌詞を忘れちまった」

そうして2匹は、アリスのまわりをぐるぐる踊り始めました。ときどき近づきすぎてアリスの足をふみつけたりしながら踊り続けました。海ガメもどきは、とてもゆっくり悲しげにこう歌いました――

「もうちょっと早く歩けない？」と、タラは巻き貝に言いました、
「イルカがうしろにつっかえて、ぼくのしっぽを踏んでるの。
みてみて、ロブスターや海ガメたちが行く、楽しそう！
みんな浜辺を歩いてる――さあ、ぼくたちも一緒に踊ろうよ？
　　踊ろう、踊らない、踊ろう、踊らない、一緒に踊ろうよ？
　　踊ろう、踊らない、踊ろう、踊らない、一緒に踊ろうよ？」

「きみにはわからないだろうけど、ぼくたち、ロブスターたちと一緒に沖に投げ込まれたら、サイコーの気分だよ！」
でも、巻き貝は答えました。「遠すぎ、遠すぎるよ！」そして目をそらしてしまいました。
それからタラにていねいにお礼を言って、ダンスは辞退しました。
　　踊らない、踊れない、踊らない、
踊れない、ダンスはご辞退。
　　踊らない、踊れない、踊らない、
踊れない、ダンスはご辞退。

"What does it matter how far we go?" his friend replied.
"There is another beach, you know, on the other side.
The farther they are from England, the nearer they are to France,
So don't turn white, lovely snail, but come and join the dance.
    Will you, won't you, will you,
        won't you, will you join the dance?
    Will you, won't you, will you,
        won't you, will you join the dance?"

"Thank you, it's a very interesting dance to watch," said Alice, feeling very happy that it had finished at last, "and I do like that strange song about the whiting!"

"Oh, yes," said the Mock Turtle, "you've seen them, of course?"

"Yes," said Alice, "I've often seen them at dinn…" She stopped herself quickly.

"I don't know where 'dinn' is," said the Mock Turtle, "but if you've seen them so often, of course you know what they are like."

"I believe so," Alice replied thoughtfully. "They have their tails in their mouths.

"You're right, they *have* their tails in their mouths, and the reason is…" Here the Mock Turtle started to feel tired so he shut his eyes. "Explain the reason to her and everything," he said to the Gryphon.

■ turn white 青くなる　■ dinn 名 dinner（夕食）の言い損ない

「遠くまで飛ばされたら困るの？」と、タラは友人の巻き貝に言いました。
「海のかなたにまた別の海岸があるんだよ。
イギリスから遠くなればなるほど、フランスに近づくんだ」
いとしい巻き貝君、青ざめていないで一緒に踊ろうよ。
　　踊ろう、踊らない、踊ろう、
　　　　　踊らない、一緒に踊ろうよ？
　　踊ろう、踊らない、踊ろう、踊らない、
　　　　一緒に踊ろうよ？

「誘ってくれてありがとう。みんなのダンスを見ているだけで楽しかったわ」と、やっとダンスが終わってくれたので、アリスはかなりホッとして言いました。「それに、タラのへんてこな歌も気に入ったわ！」

「ああ、そうだ」と、海ガメもどき。「タラは見たことがあるよね？」

「ええ」と、アリス。「しょっちゅう見てますよ。晩ごは……」と言いかけ、あわてて口をつぐみました。

「『バンゴハ』の場所は知らんが」と、海ガメもどき。「しょっちゅう見てるってことは、当然、どんな風貌かわかるよね」

「わかると思います」アリスはよく考えながら答えました。「尾を口にくわえています」

「そのとおりじゃ。タラどもは尾を口にくわえておる。そのわけはじゃな……」そろそろ海ガメもどきはくたびれてきたので、目をつぶりました。「理由を全部説明してやれ」と、グリフォンに言いました。

"The reason is," said the Gryphon, "that they *went* with the lobsters to the dance. So they got thrown out to sea. So they had to fall a long way. So they got their tails stuck in their mouths. So they couldn't get them out again. That's all."

"Thank you," said Alice, "it's very interesting. I never knew so much about a whiting before."

"I can tell you more than that, if you like," said the Gryphon. "Do you know why it is called a whiting?"

"I've never thought about it," said Alice. "Why?"

"*It cleans boots and shoes,*" the Gryphon replied very factually.

Alice did not understand. "It cleans boots and shoes," she repeated to herself.

"Why, what do you clean *your* shoes with?" said the Gryphon. "I mean, what makes them so shiny and clean?"

Alice looked down at them, and considered a little before she gave her answer. "They are cleaned with 'blacking' I believe."

"Well, boots and shoes under the sea are cleaned with whiting."

"If I'd been the whiting," said Alice, who was still thinking about the song, "I'd have said to the porpoise 'Keep back, please! We don't want *you* with us!' "

"They have to have him with them," the Mock Turtle said. "No wise fish would go anywhere without a porpoise."

■ get thrown out 放り出される　■ get stuck 詰まる　■ get out 取り出す
■ factually 副 事実に基づいて　■ consider 動 よく考える　■ blacking 名 靴墨
■ keep back （後ろに）下がる　■ wise 形 賢い

「その理由は」と、グリフォンが続けます。「つまりだな、タラたちはロブスターたちとダンスに行ってしまったんだよ。それでみんな一緒に海のかなたにポーンと投げ込まれたんだ。長い距離をずーっと落っこちたんで、あせりまくって自分の尾をがしっ口にくわえたのさ。それで二度と口から離せなくなってしまった。おしまい」

「ありがとう」と、アリス。「すごくおもしろいわ。タラのことを今までぜんぜん知らなかったから」

「もっと話してやってもいいんだよ」と、グリフォン。「どうしてタラっていうのか知っているかい？」

「考えたこともなかったわ」と、アリス。「どうして？」

「ブーツや靴をみがくのさ」と、グリフォンは、まじめに事実を語っている口調で言いました。

アリスにはチンプンカンプンでした。「ブーツや靴をみがくんですって？」と、自分自身に向かって繰り返しました。

「お嬢ちゃんは、靴をみがくとき、何を使う？」と、グリフォンが尋ねました。「つまり、どうやったら靴がぴかぴかになると思う？」

アリスはみんなを見おろして、ちょっと考えてから答えました。「『ブラッキング──靴墨』を使ってぴかぴかにするんだと思うけど」

「そうだな、ブーツや靴は、海底では黒くするブラッキングのかわりに、白くするホワイティング（たら）たちがやってくれるのさ」

「もしわたしがタラだったら」と、さっきの歌が頭から離れないアリスは言いました。「イルカにはっきり言ってやったと思うわ。『もっとうしろに下がってちょうだい！　くっついてこないで！』」

「いや、イルカと離れるわけにいかんよ」と、海ガメもどき。「かしこいサカナなら、イルカなしにどこへも行かん」

"Wouldn't it really!" cried Alice, very surprised.

"Of course not," said the Mock Turtle.

Alice did not really understand what they were talking about, but luckily the Gryphon then said, "Come now, let's hear some of *your* adventures."

"I could tell you my adventures—beginning from this morning," said Alice a little quietly; "but it's no use going back to yesterday, because I was a different person then."

"Tell us about that," said the Mock Turtle.

"No, no! The adventures first," cried the Gryphon.

So Alice began telling them all her adventures from the time when she first saw the White Rabbit. She felt a little worried because the two animals got so close to her, one on each side, and opened their eyes and mouths so *very* wide; but she felt happier as she talked. Her listeners were completely quiet until she got to the part about her talking to the Caterpillar and the words of the song all coming out wrong, and then the Mock Turtle took a big breath and said, "That's very strange!"

"It's as strange as it could be," said the Gryphon.

"The words all come out wrong," the Mock Turtle repeated thoughtfully. "I would like to hear her try and repeat something now. Tell her to begin." He looked at the Gryphon as if he thought it had some kind of power over Alice.

■ come now さあほら ■ on each side それぞれの側に ■ come out wrong 誤りという結果になる ■ have power over ～を思いのままに操る力を持っている

「ほんとうに!」と、アリスはものすごくびっくりして叫びました。

「当然じゃ」と、海ガメもどき。

アリスには、彼らの話がさっぱりわかりませんでした。でも、グリフォンが口をはさんでくれてホッとしました。「さあ、こんどはお嬢ちゃんの冒険談を聞こうじゃないか」

「わたしの冒険談を話してあげられるわ——ではまず、今朝の出来事から始めましょう」 アリスはちょっぴりおずおずとして言いました。「でも、昨日にさかのぼっても意味がないの。だってそのときのわたしは、別人だったんですもの」

「そこのところを説明してくれないか」と、海ガメもどき。

「だめだめ! 冒険のほうが先だよ」と、グリフォン。

そこでアリスは、初めて白ウサギを見つけたときに始まった冒険の数々を話しました。2匹の動物が両側からアリスにぴたっとくっついて、目と口を思いっきりあんぐりと開けているので、ちょっと落ち着きませんでしたが、話し進めるうちに気分がよくなってきました。アリスとイモムシとの会話の途中でアリスが暗唱した歌の歌詞が、全然違う言葉になってしまったくだりにさしかかるまで、聞き手たちは声もたてずにじっと聞き入っていました。海ガメもどきは長々とため息をついてこう言いました。「それは、すごくヘンだなあ!」

「そんなヘンなこと、そうそうないよね」と、グリフォン。

「全然違う言葉になってしまった」 海ガメもどきは、考えこみながら繰り返しました。「聞いてみたいもんじゃのう。この子がなにか暗唱してくれるのを。始めるように言っておくれ」と、海ガメもどきはグリフォンを向いて言いました。まるでアリスが、グリフォンの言うことを何でも聞くとでも思っているかのようでした。

"Stand up and repeat, 'It is the voice of the Lobster'," said the Gryphon.

"This is terrible, the animals are always ordering me about and making me repeat lessons!" thought Alice. "It is like being at school." However, she got up and began to repeat it, but her head was so full of the Lobster-Quadrille, that she did not know what she was saying, and the words came out very strangely indeed—

"It is the voice of the lobster, I hear him say,
You have made me too brown, I must put sugar in my way.
As a duck with its eyes, so he with his nose
Ties his belt and his buttons and turns out his toes.
When the beach is dry, he is as happy as a lark (a kind of bird)
And will talk in bad ways of the Shark (a kind of fish)
But, when the sea comes in and sharks are around,
His voice has a quiet and peaceful sound."

"That is different from what *I* used to say when I was a child," said the Gryphon.

"Well, I have never heard it before," said the Mock Turtle, "but it sounds very strange to me."

Alice said nothing, she sat down again with her face in her hands, wondering if anything would *ever* happen in the usual way again.

"I would like you to explain it to me," said the Mock Turtle.

■ duck 图 アヒル《著者と学寮長の３人の幼い娘たちのボート遊びに同行した、牧師ダックワースさんがモデル》 ■ turn out 外へ曲がる ■ lark 图 ヒバリ ■ shark 图 サメ

「立ち上がって暗唱するのだ。『ロブスターの声が聞こえる』をな」グリフォンは言いました。

「ひどいわ！　ここの動物たちときたら、しょっちゅうわたしに命令したり、おさらいをさせるんだから！」と、アリスは思いました。「これじゃあ、学校にいるのと変わらないじゃない」　それでもアリスは立ち上がって、暗唱を始めました。でも、アリスの頭の中はロブスターのカドリールダンスで一杯だったので、自分でも何を言っているのかわかりませんでした。それに、アリスの口をついて出てくるのは、どれもこれも、実にへんてこりんな言葉ばかりでした――

「ロブスターさんの声がする。こう言っている。
ぼくを焼き過ぎてくれちゃって、行くとこ砂糖をまいておかないと。
あひるはまぶたでやるけれど、ロブスターさんは鼻先で、
ベルトをしめてボタンをかけ、つま先を外へ向ける。
砂浜が乾いているときは、ひばり（鳥の一種）のように陽気で、
サメ（魚の一種）をけなしまくるのさ。
でも、潮が満ちてサメどもがうようよ寄ってくりゃ、
ロブスターさんの声は、静かに穏やかに響く」

「それは、ぼくが子どものときに口ずさんでいたのとは違うなあ」と、グリフォン。

「初めて聞いたなあ」と、海ガメもどき。「それにしてもおかしな言葉だなあ」

アリスは何も言いませんでした。だた、両手で顔をおってまたしゃがみこみ、この先また、いつも通りにすべてが起こることなんてありえるのかしらと思っていました。

「説明してくれないかな」と、海ガメもどき。

"She can't do that," said the Gryphon quickly. "Go on with the next part."

"But about his toes?" the Mock Turtle asked. "How *could* he turn them out with his nose?"

"He was dancing," said Alice, but it was very difficult for her to understand what was happening, and she wanted to talk about something different.

"Go on with the next part," the Gryphon repeated impatiently, "it begins '*I passed by his garden.*'"

Alice did not want to say it, but she felt that she had to, so she continued in a shaking voice—

"I passed by his garden, and saw, with one eye,
How the owl and the panther were sharing a pie.
The panther took some meat,
While the owl had the plate as its part of the eats
When the pie was finished, the Owl,
Was kindly allowed to take the spoon,
While the panther received the knife and fork with a grin
And finished the food by—"

"What *is* the use of repeating all that," the Mock Turtle said, "if you don't explain it as you go on? It's by far the strangest thing *I* have ever heard!"

■ go on with どんどん進める　■ impatiently 副 イライラして　■ pass by 〜のそばを通る　■ owl 名 フクロウ　■ panther 名 ヒョウ　■ share 動 分ける　■ by far はるかに、断然

「それは無理」と、すかさずグリフォンが口をはさみます。「いいから、次のとこをやってみて」

「じゃが、ロブスターのつま先はどうなっておるんだ？」と、海ガメもどきが食いさがります。「いったいぜんたい、どうやったら、ロブスターが鼻でつま先を外に向けられるのか教えてくれないか？」

「ダンスしていたからよ」と、アリス。正直言って、アリスは何がなんだかわからなくなっていました。ですから、話題を変えようと思いました。

「いいから、次のとこをやってみて」 グリフォンが、いらいらしながら繰り返します。「出だしは、『彼の庭先を通ったら』だよ」

もう暗唱なんかしたくありませんでしたが、するしかないと思えたので、アリスは震える声で先を続けました。

「彼の庭先を通ったら、片目で見えたよ、
フクロウとヒョウがパイを分けっこ。
ヒョウがお肉を、
フクロウは宴のお皿を取っただけ
パイがすっかりなくなると、フクロウは、
ぜひともスプーンをおみやげにとすすめられ、
ヒョウはナイフとフォークを受け取りニヤリと笑う
そしてパクリと食事を終わらせた——」

「そんなもの暗唱していったい何になる？」と、海ガメもどき。「ちゃんと途中で説明できんなら、今まで聞いたなかで、ぜったいに一番ヘンな話になる！」

"Yes, I think you should stop now," said the Gryphon, and Alice was very happy that they said that.

"Shall we try doing the Lobster-Quadrille again?" suggested the Gryphon. "Or would you like the Mock Turtle to sing you another song?"

"Oh, a song please, if the Mock Turtle would be so kind," Alice replied so happily that the Gryphon said (in a rather angry way) "you never know what things people like! Sing her, 'Turtle Soup' will you, old man?"

The Mock Turtle breathed deeply, and began to sing as well as he could. Sometimes he had to stop because he started crying.

> "Beautiful Soup, so rich and green
> Waiting in a hot bowl!
> Who would not eat such a lovely thing?
> Soup of the evening, beautiful soup!
> Soup of the evening, beautiful soup!
> Beau—ootiful Soo—oop !
> Beau—ootiful Soo—oop!
> Soo—oop of the evening,
> Beautiful, beautiful soup!

■ Shall we 〜しましょうか？　■ bowl 图 椀、どんぶり

Chapter X

　「たしかに、もうやめた方がいい」と、グリフォンが言ったのを聞いて、アリスはすごくほっとしました。
　「ロブスターのカドリールダンスをもう一度やってみようか？」と、グリフォンが提案しました。「それとも、海ガメもどきに別の歌をうたってもらおうか？」
　「まあ、それじゃあぜひ、歌をお願いします。海ガメもどきさんさえよろしければ」　アリスはとってもうれしそうに答えました。グリフォンは（ちょっとばかりへそを曲げて）言いました。「たで食う虫も好き好きだな！　歌ってやんなよ、じいさん。『ウミガメスープ』をな。いいだろ？」
　海ガメもどきは深呼吸をしてから、一生懸命に歌い始めました。時おりすすり泣きで声をつまらせながら。

　　「きれいなスープ、トロリとみどり
　　あつあつスープ、お皿で待ってる！
　　こんな素敵なスープ、だれが飲まずにいられよう？
　　ゆうげのスープ、きれいなスープ！
　　ゆうげのスープ、きれいなスープ！
　　　　きーれいな　スーップ！
　　　　きーれいな　スーップ！
　　ゆうげのスープ、
　　　　きれいな、きれいなスープ！

Beautiful Soup! Who cares for fish,
Meat, or any other dish?
Who would not give everything for two
Bowls of beautiful, beautiful soup
Bowls of beautiful, beautiful soup
　　Beau—ootiful Soo—oop!
　　Beau—ootiful Soo—oop!
Soo—oop of the e—e—evening,
　Beautiful, Beautiful Soup!"

"Once more!" cried the Gryphon, and the Mock Turtle had just begun to repeat it, when a cry of "The trial is beginning!" was heard in the distance.

"Come on!" cried the Gryphon, and, taking Alice's hand, it hurried off without waiting for the end of the song.

"What trial is it? Alice asked as she ran; but the Gryphon only answered. "Come on!" and ran faster. The Mock Turtle continued singing the song.

■ trial 名 裁判　■ wait for 〜を待つ

きれいなスープ！　スープさえあれば、
お肉も魚も、だれが他になにかほしがろう？
きれいな、きれいなスープ２皿のためだったら、
すべてを投げ出す。
　　きーれいな　スーップ！
　　きーれいな　スーップ！
ゆーうーげのスープ
　　きれいな、きれいなスープ！」

「もういちど！」と、グリフォンがわめきます。海ガメもどきがくり返そうとしたその時です。「裁判が始まります！」と叫ぶ声が遠くから聞こえてきました。

「おいで！」と、グリフォンは叫んで、アリスの手をつかみ、歌の終わりまで待たずに駆けだしました。

「何の裁判なの？」　アリスは走りながら聞きましたが、グリフォンはただ「おいで！」と答えて、さらにスピードをあげました。海ガメもどきは、歌い続けていました。

Chapter XI

Who Stole the Tarts?

The King and Queen of Hearts were sitting down when Alice and the Gryphon arrived. Everyone was standing round the King and Queen—all sorts of little birds and animals, as well as all the playing cards: the Knave was standing in front of them, with a guard on each side to stop him from escaping, and near the King was the White Rabbit with a piece of paper in his hand. In the very middle of the court-room was a table with a large plate of tarts on it. They looked so good that it made Alice quite hungry to look at them. "I wish they would get the trial started," she thought, "and pass round the food and drink!" But there seemed to be no chance of this; so she began looking at everything in the room.

■ tart 图 タルト ■ stand around 群れ集まって立つ ■ court-room 图 法廷 ■ get started 始める ■ pass round 配る

第 11 章
タルト泥棒は誰？

　アリスとグリフォンが到着したときには、王様と女王陛下はもう王座に着いていました。そのまわりには大群衆がひしめきあっていました——ありとあらゆる小鳥や動物たちと、トランプのカードたち。ハートのジャックが最前列にいました。ジャックが逃げないように、2人の兵士が両側から彼をはさむようにガードしています。王様のそばには、白ウサギが紙を持って立っています。法廷の真ん中には、テーブルが据えられ、タルトを盛りつけた大皿がのっています。ものすごく美味しそうで、見ているだけでつばが出てきそうでした。「早く裁判を始めないかしら」と、アリスは思いました。「そして食べ物や飲み物を配ってくれたらいいのになあ！」 でもそんな気配はみじんもありませんでした。アリスは、部屋中をつぶさに観察することにしました。

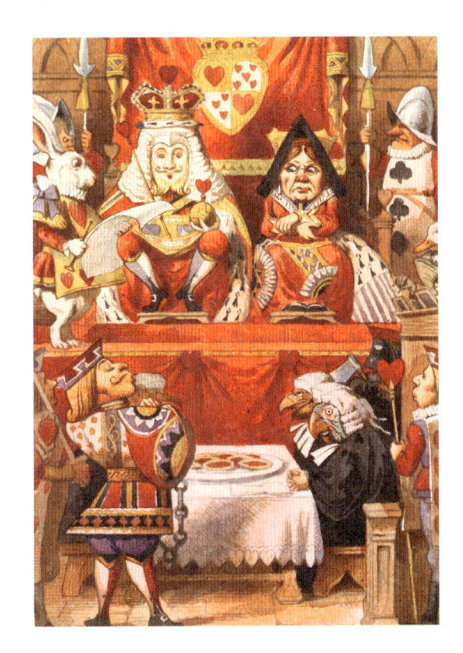

Alice had never been in a court-room before, but she had read about them in books, and she was quite pleased to find that she knew the name of nearly everything there. "That's the judge," she said to herself.

The judge was the King. "And that's the jury-box," thought Alice, "and those twelve birds and animals are the jurors." She said this last word two or three times to herself—she thought that very few girls of her age would know the meaning of it.

The twelve jurors were all writing very busily. "What are they doing?" Alice asked the Gryphon. "The trial has not started yet so they should not be writing anything."

"They're writing down their names," the Gryphon answered quickly, "in case they forget them before the end of the trial."

"How strange!" cried Alice. Then suddenly the White Rabbit shouted, "Silence in the Court!" and the King looked round to see who was talking.

Alice could see that all the jurors were writing down "How strange!" on their boards and she could even see that one of them didn't even know how to write the words and that he had to ask the juror next to him how to write it. "There will be lots of problems before the trial is over," thought Alice.

■ judge 图 裁判官　■ jury-box 图 陪審員席　■ juror 图 陪審員

Chapter XI

　法廷に入るのは初めて。でも、本で読んだことがありました。そのおかげで、そこにいる登場人物の名前をすべて知っていて、とてもうれしくなりました。「あれが裁判官ね」アリスはつぶやきました。

　裁判官は王様でした。「それから、あれが陪審員席だわ」と、アリスは思いました。「それに、あの12匹の小鳥と動物たちが陪審員ね」「陪審員」という最後の言葉を、2、3回、心の中で繰り返しました。アリスの年齢の女の子で、その言葉の意味を知っている子は、すっごく少ないだろうと思いました。

　12匹の陪審員たちはみんな、せっせとメモをとっていました。「みんな、なにをしてるのかしら？」アリスはグリフォンに尋ねました。「まだ裁判は始まっていないから、記録することなんてないわ」

　「自分の名前を書いているんだよ」と、グリフォンは、落ち着きはらって答えました。「裁判が終わるころになって、もの忘れしたら大変だから」

　「まあ、ヘンだわ！」と、アリスは叫びました。そのとき、白ウサギが突然、声を張り上げて言いました。「法廷内はご静粛に！」王様は法廷を見わたして、誰がまだしゃべっているのかを確かめようとしました。

　アリスには陪審員が全員、「まあ、ヘンだわ！」と、石板に書きつけているのが見えました。書き方がわからなくなって、隣にいる陪審員に教えてもらっている陪審員もいました。「これじゃあ裁判が終わるまでに、たくさんの問題が発生しそう。この先思いやられるわ」と、アリスは思いました。

One of the jurors had a pencil that made a noise. This, of course, Alice did *not* like, so she went round the court-room and stood behind him and very soon had a chance to take it away. She did it so quickly that the poor little juror (it was Bill the Lizard) did not understand where it had gone. So, after looking for it he had to write with one finger for the rest of the day, and this was very difficult as it left no mark on the paper.

The King then asked the White Rabbit to read the accusation. The White Rabbit held up the piece of paper that was in his hand and started reading.

"The Queen of Hearts, she made some tarts,
All on a summer's day:
The Knave of Hearts took those tarts
And took them far away!"

"What do you think we should do?" the King asked the Jury.

"Not yet! Not yet!" said the Rabbit quickly. "We can't ask them that question yet!"

■ take away 取り上げる　■ lizard 图 トカゲ　■ for the rest of ～の残りの間ずっと
■ leave a mark 跡を残す　■ accusation 图 訴状、告訴理由　■ jury 图 陪審員団

Chapter XI

　陪審員の一人が、えんぴつでキーキーと耳触りな音を立てていました。がまんできなかったので、アリスは法廷をぐるりと回り、その陪審員のうしろにしのび寄りました。すきをみて、えんぴつをさっと取り上げてしまいました。あまりにもすばやい動作だったので、あわれな小さな陪審員（トカゲのビルでした）は、えんぴつがいったいどこに消えたのか、まるでキツネにつままれたようでした。しばらく探しまわっても見つからなかったので、結局それからずっと、自分の指で書かなくてはなりませんでした。そんなことをしても、石板にはなんのあともつかないので、すごく苦労していました。

　次に王様は、白ウサギに、訴状を読めと命令しました。白ウサギは、手に持っていた紙を広げて読みあげました。

　　「ハートの女王は、タルトを焼いた、
　　　　夏の日まるごとついやして
　　　ハートのジャックはタルトを盗んだ、
　　　　まるごと持って遠くへ逃げタルト！」

「どうしたらよいかのう？」と、王様は陪審員団に聞きました。
「まだです！　まだです！」　ウサギはあわてて止めました。「陪審員にその質問を投げかける前に、まだやることがあります！」

"Call the first witness," said the King, and the White Rabbit called out, "First Witness!"

The first witness was the Hatter. He came in with a teacup in one hand and a piece of bread and butter in the other. "I am sorry, Sir," he began, "for bringing these in, but I hadn't quite finished my tea when I was told to come here."

"You should have finished," said the King. "When did you begin?"

The Hatter looked at the March Hare, who had followed him into the court, arm in arm with the Dormouse. "Fourteenth of March, I *think* it was," he said.

"Fifteenth," said the March Hare.

"Sixteenth," added the Dormouse.

"Write that down," the King said to the Jury; and they happily wrote down all three dates on their paper, and then added them up as if they were money.

"Take off your hat," the King said to the Hatter.

"It isn't mine," said the Hatter.

"Did you *take* it from someone?" shouted the King, turning to the Jury, who wrote down the fact that it wasn't the Hatter's.

"I keep them to sell," the Hatter added. "I've none of my own. I'm a Hatter."

Here the Queen began looking at the Hatter, who turned white.

"Tell us what you know," said the King, "and don't worry. If you don't I will arrange for you to be killed now."

■ witness 图 証人　■ arm in arm 腕を組んで　■ write down 書き留める、記録する　■ add up 加算する　■ take off（身につけているものを）外す　■ take from ～から取る　■ arrange for ～の準備［手配］をする

「最初の証人を呼べ」と、王様が言いました。白ウサギは叫びました。「最初の証人、これへ！」

最初の証人は、あの帽子屋でした。帽子屋は片手にティーカップを持ち、もう一方の手には一切れのバターつきパンを持って入ってきました。「どうかお許しください、陛下」と、帽子屋は切り出しました。「呼び出されたとき、まだお茶をすませていなかったものですから、こんなものを持ってまいりまして」

「すませておくべきだったな」と、王様は言いました。「お茶を始めたのはいつだ？」

帽子屋は三月ウサギの方を見て答えました。三月ウサギはヤマネと腕を組んで、帽子屋のあとについて法廷に入って来ていました。「たしか3月14日だったと思います」

「15日だった」と、三月ウサギ。

「16日だよ」と、ヤマネ。

「書きとめておけ」王様は陪審員たちに言いました。陪審員たちはうれしそうに、3つの日付を書き留めました。それから3つの数字を、まるでお金の勘定をするかのように足し算しました。

「お前の帽子を取らぬか」と、王様は帽子屋に言いました。

「わたしのではありません」と、帽子屋。

「ぬすんだのか？」王様はそう叫んで陪審員の方を向きました。陪審員はさっそく、帽子は帽子屋のものではないと記録しました。

「売り物なんです」と、帽子屋は説明を付け加えました。「自分の帽子は一つも持っておりません。なんせ、わたしは帽子屋なんで」

そこで、女王陛下が帽子屋をじろじろと眺め始めたので、彼は青ざめてしまいました。

「おまえが知っていることを述べよ」と、王様。「心配無用だ。もしなにも知らなかったとしても、すぐに処刑を命ずるからな」

This did not seem to make the Hatter feel any happier at all. He kept moving from one foot to the other, looking worriedly at the Queen, and because he was worried he bit a large piece out of his teacup instead of the bread and butter.

Just at this moment Alice felt very strange but soon she realised why. She was beginning to grow larger again, and she thought at first that she would get up and leave the room, but then she decided to stay where she was as long as there was enough room for her to sit.

"I wish you wouldn't sit so close to me," said the Dormouse, who was sitting next to her. "I can hardly breathe."

"I'm sorry," said Alice very quietly, "but I'm growing."

"You should not grow in *here*," said the Dormouse.

"Everybody has to grow somewhere," said Alice louder than before, "you know you're growing too."

"Yes, but *I* grow in the same way that everyone else does," said the Dormouse. "I'm not growing as fast as you are." And he got up very angrily and crossed over to the other side of the court.

All this time the Queen had never stopped looking at the Hatter, and, just as the Dormouse crossed the court, she said to one of the soldiers in the room, "Bring me a list of the singers!" which made the Hatter shake so much that his shoes fell off.

■ bit 動 bite（かじる）の過去形　■ everyone else 他人　■ cross over ～に越境する
■ singer 名 内通者、密告者　■ fall off ～が離れ落ちる

Chapter XI

　こんなことを言われても、帽子屋の気が休まるはずがありません。帽子屋はそわそわと体重を右足にかけたり左足にかけたりして、びくびくと女王陛下を見つめました。あんまり不安だったので、帽子屋は、バター付きパン切れの代わりに、ティーカップをバリッとかじってしまいました。

　そのとき、アリスはとても奇妙な気分におそわれました。どうしてなのかは、すぐにわかりました。またどんどん大きくなり始めていたのです。起きあがって法廷を出ようかと考えましたが、アリスが座るスペースがある限り、ここにとどまることにしました。

「そんなにぼくにくっつかないでくれよ」と、隣に座っていたヤマネが言いました。「息ができないよ」

「ごめんなさい」アリスはしょんぼりと言いました。「わたし、どんどん大きくなっているんですもの」

「こんなとこで、大きくなっちゃだめだよ」と、ヤマネ。

「そんなこと言ったって、みんな、どこかで大きくなっているんですもの」と、アリスはさっきよりも声を上げて言いました。「あなただって、成長しているのよ」

「そうだよ。でもぼくは、みんなと同じような普通のペースで大きくなっている」と、ヤマネ。「君みたいに、ものすごい勢いで成長してなんかいないよ」そう言うと、ひどくむくれて法廷の反対側に歩いて行ってしまいました。

　その間ずーっと、女王陛下は帽子屋から目を離さずにいました。ヤマネが法廷を横切ったとき、法廷内にいた兵隊の一人に命じました。「密告者の名簿をここへ！」　それを聞いた帽子屋はガタガタと震えあがって、靴が両方ともぬげ落ちてしまいました。

"Tell us what happened," the King repeated angrily, "or I'll tell the executioner to cut off your head."

"I'm a poor man," the Hatter began, in a shaky voice, "and I hadn't begun my tea about a week ago, and the March Hare said…"

"I didn't!" the March Hare said quickly.

"You did!" said the Hatter.

"I didn't!" said the March Hare.

"He says he didn't," said the King. "Don't write down that part," he told the jurors.

"Well, the Dormouse said…" the Hatter continued, looking round to see what the Dormouse would say, but the Dormouse was asleep.

"After that," continued the Hatter, "I cut some more bread and butter…"

"But what did the Dormouse say?" one of the jurors asked.

"I can't remember," said the Hatter.

"You *must* remember," said the King, "or I'll ask the executioner to cut off your head."

The Hatter felt very worried and unhappy and so he dropped his teacup and bread and butter and bowed to the King. "I'm a poor man…" he began.

"You're a *very* bad *speaker*," said the King.

One of the jurors (a guinea pig) then shouted out because he agreed with this, so the guards put him in a bag and sat on him.

■ guinea pig モルモット　■ put ~ in a bag ~を袋に入れる　■ sit on ~の上に座る

「何がおこったのか話してみよ」と、王様が怒って繰り返しました。「さもなくば、処刑人にお前の首をはねさせるぞ」

「わたしはつまらぬ者です」と、帽子屋が震える声で切り出しました。「一週間前でもまだ、ティータイムを始められなかったぐらいです。それに、三月ウサギが言ったように……」

「言ってない！」と、三月ウサギがあわてて口をはさみました。

「言った！」と、帽子屋。

「言ってないってば！」と、三月ウサギ。

「言ってないと言っておるぞ」と、王様は陪審員に向かって言いました。「そこは記録に残すな」

「あのですね。ヤマネによると……」帽子屋は続けました。さてさてヤマネは何を言いだすのやらと思い、あたりを見わたしながら話しました。でもヤマネは、すやすやとお昼寝中でした。

「それから」帽子屋が続けます。「またパンを切りとって、バターを……」

「でも、ヤマネは何と言ったんですか？」と、陪審員の一人が尋ねました。

「それが、覚えてないんですよ」と、帽子屋。

「そんなはずはない」と、王様。「覚えていなければ、処刑人にお前の首をはねさせるぞ」

帽子屋はものすごく不安になって、すっかり落ちこみ、ティーカップをガチャンと床に落としてしまいました。バター付きパンも床の上。王様にお辞儀をして言いました。「わたしはつまらない者です……」

「お前の話はたしかに、つまらないものだ」と、王様。

陪審員の一人（モルモット）が、そのとおり！とばかり、歓声をあげたので、護衛兵たちがモルモットを袋に放り込み、その上にどっかりと腰をおろしました。

"If that is all you know," said the King, "you may go now."

Then another guinea pig juror shouted, and he was also put in a bag and sat on by the guards.

"I'd like to finish my tea," said the Hatter looking at the Queen, who was reading the list of singers.

"You may go," said the King and the Hatter quickly left the Court without even waiting to put on his shoes again.

"...and just take his head off outside," the Queen added to one of the guards; but the Hatter had disappeared before the guard could get to the door.

"Call the next witness!" said the King. The next witness was the Duchess' cook. She carried the pepper-box in her hand, and Alice guessed who it was even before she got into the Court by the way the people near the door suddenly began sneezing all at the same time.

"Tell us what you know," said the King.

"I won't," said the cook.

The King looked at the White Rabbit, who said in a low voice, "You must ask *this* witness some questions."

"Well, if I must, I must," said the King and after moving his arms and looking at the cook for a long time he asked loudly, "What are tarts made of?"

■ You may go. 行ってよし。　■ put on ～を身につける　■ pepper-box 图 コショウ入れ

Chapter XI

「お前が知っているのはそれだけか？」と、王様。「もう行ってよし」

すると、もう一匹のモルモット陪審員が、突然歓声を上げました。彼もまた、袋に放り込まれ、護衛兵たちの尻に敷かれました。

「お茶をすませてしまいたいのですが」帽子屋は、密告者のリストをながめている女王陛下を見て言いました。

「下がってよし」と、王様が言ったので、帽子屋は、ぬげた靴もはかずに、法廷を、ほうほうのていで、あとにしました。

「……外に出たら、やつの首をはねておしまい」と、女王陛下が護衛兵の一人に追加の命令を下しました。でも、護衛兵が法廷の扉に近づいたころには、帽子屋の姿は、跡かたもなく消えていました。

「次の証人を呼べ！」と、王様。次の証人は、公爵夫人の料理人でした。彼女はコショウ入れを手に持っていました。アリスは、彼女が法廷に入って来る前から、扉の近くにいた人たちがいっせいにくしゃみを始めたので、すぐにだれだかわかりました。

「知っていることを述べよ」と、王様。

「言いません」と、料理人。

王様が白ウサギを見ると、白ウサギは低い声で言いました。「この証人に、尋問せねばなりませんぞ」

「せねばならぬなら、せねばならぬな」と、王様。両腕を動かし、かなりの間料理人をじっと見つめたあと、王様は大声で尋ねました。「タルトはなんでできておる？」

"Pepper, mostly," said the cook.

"Treacle," said a sleepy voice behind her.

"Take that Dormouse!" the Queen cried out. "Kill that Dormouse! Take him away!"

For some minutes everyone in the court room was very busy taking the Dormouse away, and by the time they had settled down again the cook had disappeared.

"Never mind!" said the King happily. "Call the next witness." And he added quietly to the Queen, "Really, my dear, *you* must talk to the next witness. It makes my head hurt!"

Alice watched the White Rabbit as he looked down the list of witnesses. She was interested to know who the next witness would be "because they have not got much information *yet*," she thought.

Imagine her surprise when the White Rabbit read out the name "Alice!"

■ mostly 副 主に、ほとんど　■ settle down 落ち着く　■ never mind 気にするな
■ imagine 動 想像する、推測する　■ read out 読み上げる

「コショウだね。主に」と、料理人。

「糖蜜だようー」と、料理人の背後から、眠そうな声。

「そのヤマネを連行しろ！」と、女王陛下は叫びました。「そのヤマネを処刑せよ！　連行しろ！」

それから数分間、法廷中、ヤマネを追い出すのに上を下への大さわぎになってしまい、やっとおさまったころには、料理人の姿は跡かたもなく消えていました。

「まあいい！」と、王様は陽気に言いました。「次なる証人を連れてまいれ」それから、女王陛下に向かってささやきました。「なあ、おまえ。次はおまえが証人と話しておくれ。わしの頭はがんがん張り裂けそうじゃ！」

アリスは、白ウサギが証人リストを読んでいるのを見つめながら、次の証人はいったい誰かしら、と思いました。「だって、まだほとんど情報を得てはいないんですもの」

想像してみてください。白ウサギが、「アリス！」という名前を読み上げたとき、どんなにアリスが驚いたかを。

Chapter XII

Alice's Evidence

"Here!" cried Alice loudly forgetting in the interest of the moment how large she had grown in the last few minutes. She jumped up in such a hurry that she hit the juror's box with the edge of her skirt, so all the jurors fell on to the heads of the people below, and they lay there altogether on the floor.

"Oh, I am very sorry!" she cried, and she began picking them up again as quickly as she could and putting them back in their box.

"The trial cannot go on," said the King in a very loud voice, "until all the jurors are back in their seats—*all* of them," he repeated very loudly, looking straight at Alice as he said so.

■ evidence 名 証言 ■ in the interest of ～の関係で ■ in a hurry 慌てて
■ altogether 副 みんな一緒に ■ look straight at ～をまっすぐ見つめる

第12章

アリスの証言

「はい！」思わずアリスは大声で返事をしました。とつぜんのことに気がせいて、この数分の間に自分がどれほど大きくなってしまったのかをすっかり忘れていたのです。あんまりあわてて立ちあがったので、スカートのすそで陪審席をひっくりかえし、陪審員は全員、下にいた人たちの頭上にころげおちてしまいました。みんな一緒に、床の上でバタバタと横たわっています。

「まあ、ほんとうにごめんなさい！」と叫ぶと、アリスは大急ぎで陪審員を一匹ずつつまみ上げ、もとの席にもどしてあげました。

「このままでは裁判を進めるわけにいかん」と、王様が叫びました。「陪審員全員が席にもどるまでは──全員がな」と、アリスをにらみつけながら、大声で繰り返しました。

Alice looked at the juror's box and saw that she had put Bill the Lizard in with his head downwards, and the poor little thing was moving its tail about in a sad way because it was unable to move in the box. She soon got it out again and put it right, "not that it makes much difference," she thought to herself, "I should think it would be as much use in the trial with its tail up as with its head up.

As soon as the jury had recovered from the surprise of being hit, and their paper and pencils had been found and given back to them, they started to work very hard and to write the story of what had happened. The lizard seemed too surprised to do anything except sit with his mouth open and look up to the roof of the court room.

"What do you know about this business?" the King asked Alice.

"Nothing," said Alice.

"Nothing *at all*?" asked the King.

"Nothing *at all*," replied Alice.

"That's very important," the King said, turning to the jurors.

They were just beginning to write this down on their paper when the White Rabbit said, "*Un*important, you mean sir," very politely but making strange faces at him as he spoke.

"*Un*important, of course, I meant," the King quickly said and went on to say to himself in a quieter voice, "important—unimportant—unimportant—important…" as if he was trying to decide which word sounded best.

■ unable to 〜することができない　■ put 〜 right 〜を正しい状態にする　■ recover 動 回復する　■ business 名 状況、問題　■ unimportant 形 取るに足りない

Chapter XII

　アリスが陪審員席を見ると、トカゲのビルを頭からさかさにつっこんでしまったことに気づきました。哀れなちびちゃんは身動きがとれず、しっぽを悲しげにふってもがいていました。アリスはすぐにビルを引っぱり出して、もとにもどしてあげました。「もどしたからってあんまり変わりはないでしょうけどね」と、アリスはひとりごと。「しっぽが上でも頭が上でも、裁判には関係なさそうだし」

　ひっくりかえったショックから陪審員が立ち直り、石板やエンピツが見つかって陪審員の手元にもどされたとき、陪審員たちは、たった今起こった出来事をけんめいに記録し始めました。トカゲはまだショックから立ちなおることができず、口をあんぐりと開けて、法廷の天井を見つめていました。

「この件について何を知っておる？」と、王様はアリスに尋ねました。
「何も知りません」と、アリス。
「まったく何も知らないのじゃな？」と、王様。
「まったく何も知りません」と、アリス。
「それは極めて重要だ」と王様は言って、陪審員の方を見ました。
　陪審員が記録し始めたそのとき、白ウサギが口をはさみました。「重要ではない、という意味でしょうか、陛下」　丁寧な口調でしたが、顔をしかめて王様を見つめながら言いました。
「重要ではない、当然、そういう意味じゃ」と、王様はあわてて答えました。そしてすぐに、低い声でつぶやきました。「重要――重要ではない――重要――重要ではない……」　まるでどちらの言葉の方が響きがよいのか、確かめているようでした。

Some of the jurors wrote down 'important' and some wrote down 'unimportant'. Alice could see this, as she was near enough to look, "but it doesn't make any difference," she thought to herself.

At this moment, the King, who had been for some time busily writing in his notebook, called out, "Silence!" and read out from his book, "Rule forty two. *All persons more than a mile high are to leave the court.*"

Everybody looked at Alice.

"*I'm* not a mile high," said Alice.

"You are," said the King. "You're nearly two miles high," added the Queen.

"Well, I won't go," said Alice, "because that is not a real rule; you only thought of it just now."

"It is the oldest rule in the book," said the King.

"Then it should be number One," said Alice.

The King turned white and shut his notebook quickly. "Think about your decision," he said to the Jury in a low, shaky voice.

"There's more for the jurors to hear. They can't decide yet, sir," said the White Rabbit jumping up in a great hurry. "I have just picked up this piece of paper."

"What is in it?" asked the Queen.

"I haven't opened it yet," said the White Rabbit, "but it seems to be a letter written by the Knave to somebody."

"It must have been written to somebody," said the King.

■ mile 名 マイル《長さの単位、約1609m》

Chapter XII

　陪審員の中には、「重要だ」と記録した者もいれば、「重要ではない」と記録した者もいました。アリスは陪審員席のすぐそばにいたので、それが見えました。「どっちだっていいじゃないの」と、アリスはつぶやきました。

　ちょうどその時、しばらくせっせと自分のノートに書き込んでいた王様が、叫びました。「静粛に！」　そして、王様の本から読みあげました。「第42条。何びとであれ、身長1マイルを超える者は、この法廷から退去すべし」

　みんながアリスを見つめました。

　「わたしは1マイルもありません」と、アリス。

　「あるぞよ」と王様。「2マイル近くあるぞよ」と、女王陛下が付け加えました。

　「いずれにしても、わたしは、ここから出て行くつもりはありません」と、アリス。「なぜなら、それは正式な法律ではないからです。あなたがとっさに思いついたものでしょう」

　「これはこの法律書における、最古の規則じゃ」と、王様。

　「それなら第1条のはずでしょう」と、アリス。

　王様はすーっと青ざめて、ノートをぱたんと閉じると、陪審員に向かって、低く震える声で命じました。「評決を審議せよ」

　「まだ証言がございます。それまで評決はできません、陛下」白ウサギが大あわてで跳び上がって言いました。「この文書がたった今入手できました」

　「なんと書いてあるのじゃ？」と、女王陛下。

　「まだ開封しておりません」と、白ウサギ。「しかし、どうやら、ジャックが誰かに宛ててしたためた手紙のようでございます」

　「だれかに宛てたものに違いないのう」と、王様。

"Who is it addressed to?" asked one of the jurors.

"It isn't addressed at all," said the White Rabbit. "In fact, there is nothing written on the *outside*." He opened the paper as he spoke and added, "It isn't a letter, after all, it's a poem."

"Is it in the Knave's handwriting?" asked another of the jurors.

"No, it's not," said the White Rabbit, "and that is the strangest thing about it." (The jurors didn't seem to understand this at all.)

"He must have written it copying someone else's handwriting," said the King. (The jurors all looked happier again.)

"Please, sir," said the Knave, "I didn't write it, and they can't say that I did, there is no name signed at the end."

"If you didn't write it," said the King, "that only makes the problem worse. You *must* have wanted to make a problem or else you would have written your name like an honest man."

Everybody smiled because this was the first clever thing that the King had said.

"That *proves* he did it," said the Queen, "so cut off…"

"It doesn't prove anything!" said Alice. "You don't even know what is written on the paper!"

"Read it!" said the King.

The White Rabbit picked up the paper. "Where shall I begin, sir?" he asked.

"Begin at the beginning," the King said very strongly, "and go on till you come to the end. Then stop."

■ address 動 宛名を書く　■ after all 結局のところ　■ handwriting 名 筆跡　■ or else あるいは　■ honest 形 正直な　■ prove 動 〜を証明する

「宛先は？」と、陪審員の一人が尋ねました。

「宛先はまったくありません」と、白ウサギ。「事実、表書は白紙なのです」白ウサギはその手紙を開封しながら付け加えました。「これは手紙ではありませんでした。一編の詩です」

「それはジャックの筆跡か？」と、もう一人の陪審員が聞きました。

「いや、違います」と、白ウサギ。「まったくもって、そこが最も奇妙なことでございます」（誰一人として、状況が理解できる陪審員はいませんでした。）

「被告人は他の何者かの筆跡をまねて書いたに違いない」と、王様が言いました。（陪審員はみなそろって、ぱっと明るい顔になりました。）

「おそれながら、陛下」と、ジャックが言いました。「わたしは書いておりません。それに、最後にだれの署名もないので、わたしが書いたという証拠になりません」

「もしおまえが署名をしなかったとすると」と、王様。「それはさらに由々しき問題である。正直に署名しなかったのは、由々しき問題を発生したかったからに違いない」

全員がにっこり笑いました。この日初めて王様が口にした、気の利いた発言だったからです。

「これで有罪と証明されたわけじゃな」と、女王陛下。「では、こやつの首を……」

「そんなの、何の証拠にもなっていないわ！」と、アリス。「だいたいそこに何が書かれているのかも知らないくせに！」

「読みあげよ！」と、王様。

白ウサギは紙を手に取り、尋ねました。「陛下、どこから始めましょうか？」

「最初から始めよ」と、王様がもったいぶって言いました。「そして終わりまで続け、終わりで終われ」

There was silence in the room while the White Rabbit read out these words—

"They told me you had been to her,
　　　And told him about me
She said I was a good person
　　　But that I could not swim.

He told them I had not gone
　　　(We know it is true)
If she should want this to go on,
　　　What would happen to you?
I gave her one, they gave him two,
　　　You gave us three or more,
They were all returned from him to you,
　　　Though they were mine before.

If she or I should happen to be
　　　Part of this affair
He hopes you will set them free
　　　Exactly as we were.

My idea was that you had been
　　　(Before she had this trouble)

■ affair 名 事件、出来事　■ exactly 副 その通りに、まさしく

Chapter XII

しーんと静まりかえった法廷で、白ウサギは、こんな詩を読みあげました。

「彼らの話では、きみは彼女のところへ行き、
　　　　僕のことを彼にしゃべったんだって
僕はいい人だけど
　　　　泳げないのよって彼女が言ったそう。

彼は、僕は行かなかったと彼らに伝えたけど
　　　　（僕らはそれが本当だって知っている）
もし彼女がことを進めたいと願ったら、
　　　　きみはいったいどうなるの？
僕は彼女に一つあげ、彼らは彼に二つあげ、
　　　　きみはぼくらに三つかそれ以上くれたけど、
すべて彼から君にもどされた、
　　　　もともとみんな、僕のものだったのに。

もし彼女か僕のどちらかがたまたま
　　　　この事態の巻きぞえを食らえば
君が彼らを自由にすることを彼は望むだろう
　　　　昔のまんまの僕らにもどしてくれることを。

僕が思ったのは、君がこれまで
　　　　（彼女がこの問題を起こす前）

> *A problem that came between*
> *Him, and ourselves, and it.*
>
> *Don't let him know she liked him best.*
> *For this must always be*
> *A secret, kept from all the rest*
> *Between yourself and me."*

"That's the most important thing we've heard yet," said the King happily, "so now let the jurors…"

"If any one of them can tell us about it," said Alice (she had grown so large in the last few minutes that she wasn't at all afraid of speaking). "I'll give him six pence. *I* don't believe there's any meaning in it."

The jurors all wrote down on their paper, "*She* doesn't believe there is any meaning in it," but none of them tried to understand what she had said.

"If there's no meaning in it," said the King, "that saves a lot of trouble you know, as we needn't try to find any. And yet I don't know," he went on—putting the piece of paper on his leg and looking at it with one eye. "I seem to see some meaning in them, after all. '—*said I could not swim*—' you can't swim, can you?" he added, turning to the Knave.

■ pence 图 ペンス《貨幣単位、pennyの複数形》 ■ save trouble 手間を省く

割り込んで邪魔していた問題なんだ
　　　　彼と、僕らと、それとの間に割り込んで。

　　彼女が一番好きだったのは彼だなんて、
　　　　決して彼に知らせてはいけないよ。
　　だってこれはぜったいに誰も知らない秘密にしとかなきゃいけないよ
　　　　君と僕だけの」

「これは我々がこれまで聞いた中で、もっとも重要な証拠じゃ」と、王様が上機嫌で言いました。「では、陪審員はそろそろ評決に……」
「誰か一人でも今の詩を説明できたら」と、アリス（この数分間でまたすごく大きくなっていたので、びくびくしないで発言できたのです）。「6ペンスあげるわ。この詩には意味のかけらもないと思うわ」

　陪審員たちはいっせいにカリカリと記録しました。「彼女はこの詩に意味のかけらもないと思う」　でもだれも、アリスが言いたかったことを理解しようとはしませんでした。
「意味がないと言うのなら」と、王様。「手間が省けて大助かり。なにしろ意味を探す必要がなくなるからな。じゃが、はて、どうかのう」と、膝の上に詩を広げ、片目で眺めながら続けました。「どうやら、何やら意味がありそうにわしには見えるのじゃが。『——泳げないのよって彼女が言った——』お前、泳げぬであろう？」とジャックに向き直りました。

The Knave shook his head sadly. "Do I look as if I can?" (He certainly didn't because he was made of paper.)

"All right so far," said the King, and he went on saying the poem to himself. "*'We know it to be true—'* that is the jurors, of course—*'If she should want this to go on'*—that must be talking about the Queen—*'What would happen to you?'*—What, indeed!—*'I gave her one, they gave him two'*—that must be what he did with the tarts, you know—"

"But it goes on *'They were all returned from him to you,'*" said Alice.

"Why, there they are!" said the King, happily pointing to the tarts on the table. "Nothing can be clearer than *that*. Then again—*'Before she had this trouble'*—you have never had any problems have you?" he asked the Queen.

"Never!" said the Queen angrily, throwing an inkpot at one of the jurors. (The unlucky juror was Bill the Lizard. He had stopped writing on his paper with one finger because he found it didn't make a mark, but he now quickly began again, using the ink that was coming down his face—for as long as it lasted.)

"Then the words aren't *right* for you," said the King looking round the court-room with a smile. There was complete silence.

"Let the jury tell us what they think," the King said for about the twentieth time that day. "No, no!" said the Queen. "The jurors can tell us what they think after we have decided what to do with the Knave."

■ There they are. そこにあります。　■ inkpot 名 インク入れ　■ unlucky 形 不運な
■ come down 下に落ちる

Chapter XII

　ジャックは悲しげに首を横に振りました。「泳げそうに見えますか？」（紙でできているので、泳げるはずがありません。）
　「ここまではよし」と王様。そしてぶつぶつと、詩の一部を暗唱しました。「『僕らはそれが本当だって知っている──』これは無論、陪審員たちのことだ──『もし彼女がことを進めたいと願ったら』──これは女王のことを指しているに違いない──『きみはいったいどうなるの？』──いったい、どうなるのじゃ！──『僕は彼女に一つあげ、彼らは彼に二つあげ』──これは彼がタルトをどうしたかってことに違いないだろうが──」
　「でも、まだ続いています。『すべて彼から君にもどされた』とね」と、アリスが口をはさみます。
　「あれまあ、ここにあるではないか！」と、テーブルの上に置かれたタルトを指さし、王様はうれしそうに言いました。「これですべて明白じゃ。それからまた──『彼女がこの問題を起こす前』──これまで問題など起こしたことがないじゃろ？」と、女王陛下に尋ねました。
　「一度だってありません！」と言い、女王陛下は憤慨して、インクのつぼを陪審員の一人に向かって投げつけました。（不運な陪審員は、トカゲのビルでした。自分の石板に指で記録しようとして、あとがつけられずにあきらめていましたが、インクが飛んできたので、顔からしたたり落ちるインクを使って、すぐさま記録を再開しました──インクがある限りね）
　「ということは、この言葉はお前にそぐわない」と、王様は言い、笑みを浮かべて法廷を見わたしました。みんな、シーンとしたままです。
　「陪審員は、評決を取りまとめよ」と、王様は言いました。今日20回目ぐらいです。「ダメ、ダメ！」と、女王陛下。「ジャックの処分を我々が決めてから、陪審員の評決よ」

"No, they can't!" said Alice loudly. "You can't do that!"

"Be quiet!" said the Queen turning red.

"I won't!" said Alice.

"Cut off her head!" the Queen shouted at the top of her voice. Nobody moved.

"Who cares about you?" said Alice (she had grown to her full size now). "You're nothing but a group of cards!"

When they heard this they all stood up and started rushing down towards her; she gave a little cry, feeling a bit afraid and angry and tried to get them away from her and found herself lying by the river with her head on her sister's leg. Her sister was gently brushing away some dead leaves that had come down from the trees onto Alice's face.

■ at the top of one's voice 声を限りに　■ full size 実物大の　■ brush away 〜を（ブラシなどで）払う　■ dead leaf 枯れ葉

Chapter XII

「そんなの絶対にダメよ！」と、アリスはどなりました。「絶対にダメ！」
「お黙り！」女王陛下は顔を真っ赤にして言いました。
「黙りません！」と、アリスも負けてはいません。
「あやつの首をはねよ！」と、女王陛下は声をひっくり返して叫びましたが、誰も動きません。
「あなたの言うことを聞く者がここにいるのかしら？」と、アリス（すっかり元の大きさにもどっていました）。「あんたたちはただのトランプじゃないの！」

それを聞いたとたん、すべてのトランプが立ちあがって、アリスめがけて一斉に突進してきました。アリスは怖いのと頭にきたのとで、きゃっと小さな叫び声を上げ、次々と襲ってくるトランプたちを払いのけようとしました。その瞬間、アリスは川べりで横になって、お姉さんの膝に頭をのせていました。お姉さんは、アリスの顔の上に舞い降りてくる落ち葉を、やさしくはらいのけてくれています。

"Wake up, Alice dear!" said her sister. "Why, what a long sleep you've had!"

"Oh, I've had such a strange dream!" said Alice, and she told her sister as much as she could remember of all her strange adventures, and when she had finished her sister kissed her and said, "It *was* a strange dream, dear, certainly; but now run into the house and have your tea; it's getting late." So Alice got up and ran off, thinking while she ran what a wonderful dream it had been.

But her sister sat still, just as Alice had left her, with her head on her hand, watching the sun go down and thinking of little Alice and all her wonderful adventures. Soon she too began dreaming in the same way and this was her dream—

First, she dreamed of little Alice; once again, Alice's small hands were held round her leg and the bright, lively eyes were looking up into hers—she could hear her voice, and see that strange little movement of her head to keep back the hair that *would* always get into her eyes. But as she listened, or seemed to listen, everything around her became alive with the strange people of her little sister's dream.

■ It's getting late.　もう遅い時間です。　■ with one's head on one's hand　頬杖をついて

「目をさまして、アリスちゃん！」と、お姉さんは言いました。「ずいぶんと長い間、ぐっすりと眠っていたわね！」

「まあ、わたしったら、今ものすごくヘンな夢を見ていたの！」と言ってアリスは、お姉さんに、思い出せる限りくわしく、不思議な冒険の話をしました。アリスが話し終えると、お姉さんはアリスにキスをして言いました。「アリスちゃん、ほんとうに不思議な夢を見たのね。でもそろそろおうちに帰って、お茶をいただいてらっしゃいな。遅くなってしまうわよ」そこでアリスは起き上がって駆け出しました。走りながら、なんて素敵な夢を見たんでしょうって、思いました。

お姉さんは、アリスが帰ったあとも一人残ってじっと座ったまま、頬杖をついて夕陽を眺めていました。妹の不思議な冒険に思いを馳せていました。そのうち、お姉さんもまた、つられて夢を見始めました。こんな夢です──

初めに夢に出てきたのは、ちっちゃなアリスでした。アリスは愛くるしい両手でお姉さんの膝に抱きつき、キラキラと輝くつぶらな瞳で、お姉さんの眼を下からじっとのぞきこんでいます──アリスの声がよみがえり、おくれ毛が目に入りそうになるときに小さな頭をちょっと振りやる、あの独特のしぐさまで目に浮かんできました。お姉さんが耳をすまし、聞こえてくるような気がしてさらに耳をすませていると、まわりのすべてが、幼い妹の夢に登場した不思議な生きものたちの気配とともにいきいきと息づき始めました。

The long grass moved at her feet as the White Rabbit hurried by—the frightened Dormouse made a noise as he ran past to the pool nearby. She could hear the sound of the teacups as the March Hare and his friends shared their never-ending meal, and the high voice of the Queen ordering her unlucky guests to be killed—once more the pig-baby was sneezing on the Duchess's leg, while plates were being thrown around it. Once more the cry of the Gryphon filled the air, mixed up with the distant cry of the unhappy Mock Turtle.

So she sat with closed eyes and half believed that she was in Wonderland, though she knew that if she opened her eyes again, everything would change back to reality. The grass would only be moving in the wind, and the water also—the sound of teacups would change to the sound of the bells on the farm animals and the Queen's loud cries to the voice of the farm boy. The cry of the baby and of the Gryphon and all the other strange noises would change (she knew) to the sounds of the busy farm-yard.

Lastly, she pictured to herself how this same little sister of hers would, in years to come, be a grown woman, and how she would keep, through all her later years, the simple and loving heart of her childhood, and how she would talk to other little children and make *their* eyes bright and happy with her strange stories. Perhaps she would tell them about her dream of Wonderland of long ago, and she would understand all their sadnesses and find happinesses in all their joys, remembering her own childlife and her happy summer days.

■ never-ending 形 終わることのない ■ reality 名 現実 ■ farm animal 家畜
■ picture 動 心に描く ■ joy 名 喜び ■ child-life 名 子ども時代

Chapter XII

　白ウサギが駆け抜けると、背の高い草が足元でなびきました。びっくりしたヤマネが近くの水たまりをぱしゃぱしゃ渡っていきます。三月ウサギと仲間たちが果てしないお茶会をしながら、ティーカップをカチャカチャいわせている音も聞こえてきます。不運なお客たちの首をはねよと命じている、女王陛下の金切り声も耳に響き――さらには、お皿がそこら中飛び交うなか、公爵夫人の膝の上でブタの赤ん坊がクシャミをしています。そして再び、遠くからかすかに聞こえてくる不幸な海ガメもどきのむせび泣きに交じって、グリフォンの鳴き声が響き渡ります。

　お姉さんは目を閉じて座ったまま、自分も不思議の国にいるんだと、なかば信じていました。もし目を開いたら、すべてまた、現実にひきもどされてしまうとわかっていたからです。草は風が吹いたときにだけなびき、水音も――それにティーカップの音も、農家の家畜の首にぶら下がったベルのカランコロンに変わってしまうし、女王陛下の金切り声も農家の少年の声に変わってしまう。赤ん坊の泣き声も、グリフォンや他の連中が立てるありとあらゆる不思議な音もぜんぶ――(そう、彼女にはわかっていました)――活気あふれる農家のざわめきへと変化してしまうことを。

　最後に、お姉さんは思い描いてみました。あの小さな妹が、いつの日か一人の女性として成長し、そして年を重ねてもなお、無垢で澄み渡ったやさしい心を持ち続けることを。そのときアリスはきっと、幼い子供たちに不思議なお話をして、彼らの瞳をキラキラと輝かせ、わくわくさせていることでしょう。もしかしたら、ずっと昔に夢見た、この不思議の国の夢のお話をしてあげるかもしれません。そのとき、子供たちが抱くせつない思いを受けとめ、子供たちの喜びに心震わせることでしょう。そして、少女時代のあの幸福な夏の日々を懐かしみ、思いを馳せることでしょう。

覚えておきたい英語表現

> "The words came out wrong," the Mock Turtle repeated thoughtfully. (p.180, 20行目)
> 「全然違う言葉になってしまった」海ガメもどきは、考えこみながら繰り返しました。

【解説】the Mock Turtle（海ガメもどき）は、著者キャロルが、mock turtle soup（ニセ海ガメスープ）の名前からつくりあげたものです。turtle soup（海ガメスープ）の材料はgreen turtle（アオウミガメ）ですが、高価なので、代わりに子牛の頭などが使われていたそうです。

come out ~ は、「~な結果となる」や、「意味がよくわかる」という意味で使われます。

thoughtfullyには、「深く考えて」や、「思慮深く」の意味があります。

【例文】① The photo came out well. 　　よく写ってる。

② My father smiled thoughtfully. 　　父は思いやりあふれる笑顔を見せた。

> "Tell her to begin." He looked at the Gryphon as if he thought it had some kind of power over Alice. (p.180, 22行目)
> 「彼女に始めるように言っておくれ」と、海ガメもどきはグリフォンを向いて言いました。まるでアリスが、グリフォンの言うことを何でも聞くとでも思っているかのようでした。

【解説】グリフォンは、ギリシャ神話に登場する伝説の怪獣です。ワシの頭と翼、ライオンの胴体を持つとされ、オックスフォード大学トリニティー学寮の紋でもありました。have some kind of power over ~ は、~に対して何らかのパワー・影響力を行使できるという意味です。

【例文】① Some leaders believe they have the absolute power over people.
　　　　人々に対して、自分が絶対的権力を持つと信じている指導者がいる。

② When you serve the greater good, you will have the power over your own destiny.
　　　　より大きな善のために尽くすとき、運命を左右するパワーを有する。

> "Oh, a song please, if the Mock Turtle would be so kind."
> （p.186, 6行目）
> 「まあ、それじゃあぜひ、歌をお願いします。海ガメさんさえよろしければ」

【解説】If 〜 would be so kind.「〜さんがよろしければ」は、大変礼儀正しい表現ですので、人に何か依頼するとき、ぜひ使ってみましょう。kind（やさしい）は、色々な場面で使える、優しい響きをもつ言葉です。kind weather（心地よい天気）のように、人以外にも使えます。

【例文】①It is very kind of you to bring such a wonderful gift.
素敵なプレゼントを持ってきてくださって、御心遣いに感謝します。

②I would love to see you at the reception, if you would be so kind to come.
レセプションにいらしてくださったら、すごくうれしいです。

＊相手の都合を気遣っていますが、「是非いらしてください」という思いを込めた表現です。ビジネスでも使える、相手に敬意をはらった上品な英語ですので、ぜひ覚えておきましょう。

> "I keep them to sell," the Hatter added. （p.196, 20行目）
> 「売り物なんです」と、帽子屋は説明を加えました。

【解説】この帽子屋は、オックスフォード近郊にモデルがいたとされます。いつもシルクハットをかぶっていた家具屋のカーターは、the Mad Hatterと呼ばれ、奇抜な発明をすることで有名でした。寝ている人を床の上に放り投げて起こす「目覚ましベッド」は、1851年のロンドン万国博に陳列されました。

王様が、"Take off your hat."（お前の帽子を取らぬか）と、王様の前でも脱帽しない無礼な帽子屋のマナー無視をとがめると、帽子屋は、"It isn't mine."（わたしのではありません）と、返答します。ここで愉快なのは、王様のyour hatとは、所有者がだれであっても、たまたまそのときかぶっている者の帽子を指しています。一方帽子屋は、自分は帽子の"所有者"ではないと主張します。ならば、「盗品」か？と、問い詰める王様に対して、帽子屋は、「売り物」だと答えています。非常にシンプルな英語ですが、的を得ています。I keep（名詞）to（目的語）の構文です。名詞（帽子）を保有し

覚えておきたい英語表現

ている理由は、to sell（売るため）という意味になります。keep（保有）であり、own（所有）ではないのです。

【例文】①I keep photos to remember the past.
　　　　過去の記憶を残すために写真を保存しています。

　　　②I earn money to spend.
　　　　お金を使うために稼いでいます。

"I wish you wouldn't sit so close to me," said the Dormouse, who was sitting next to her. "I can hardly breathe."（p.198, 9行目）
「そんなにぼくにくっつかないでくれよ」と、隣に座っていたヤマネが言いました。「息ができないよ」

【解説】dormouse（ヤマネ）は、冬眠が長いことから、「眠たがりや」の意味もあります。I wish you wouldn't～は、「～しないでくれるといいんだけど」や、「～されると困るんだけど」と言いたいときに、相手を気遣って、できるだけ丁寧に伝えたいときに使える便利な表現です。Don't～！「～するな！」よりも、ずっと、"オトナ"の表現です。can hardly～は、「～がやっとのことでできる」「ほとんどできない」の意味になります。

【例文】①I wish you wouldn't say such a thing.
　　　　そんな（ひどい）ことを言わないでほしい。

　　　②I can hardly imagine him dance!
　　　　彼がダンスしているところなんて、想像できない！

---

and by the time they had settled down again the cook disappeared.（p.204, 6行目）
やっとおさまったころには、料理人の姿は跡かたもなく消えていました。

【解説】settle downには、「落ち着く」と言う意味があります。騒ぎだけではなく、「所帯」をもって落ち着く、「定職」について落ち着く、居場所を見つけて落ち着く等の意味もあります。不安定な状態から脱して、安定した状況になることを指します。

【例文】① It's about time for you to settle down and have a family.
　　　　そろそろお前も身を固めて、家庭を持つべきだ。

　　　　② I don't want to settle down, I want to navigate my life and explore the world!
　　　　まだまだ落ち着きたくない。自分の人生の舵を取り、世界を探求したいんだ。

"Never mind!" （p.204, 8行目）
「まあいい！」

【解説】Never mind. は、構わない、どうでもいい、心配するな、といった意味で、カジュアルな口語体としてよく使われます。状況や相手を見極めて使いましょう。

【例文】① A：Should I call the police?
　　　　　　「警察を呼ぼうか？」
　　　　　 B：Never mind. He'll be back before we know it.
　　　　　　「大丈夫。そのうち帰ってくるよ」

　　　　② Never say never again.
　　　　絶対になんて、もう絶対に言わないで。

　　　　＊ Never Say Never Again は、初代007を演じたショーン・コネリーが、久々にボンド役に復帰して話題となった作品名です。コネリーの妻が、「もうボンドを演じないなんて言わないで（ネバーセイ・ネバーアゲイン）」と言ったことから生まれたタイトルだとされています。

Perhaps she would tell them about her dream of Wonderland of long ago, and she would understand all their sadnesses and find happinesses in all their joys, remembering her own child-life and her happy summer days. （p.224, 21行目）

もしかしたら、ずっと昔に夢見た、この不思議の国の夢のお話をしてあげるかもしれません。そのとき、子供たちが抱くせつない思いを受けとめ、子供たちの喜びに心震わせることでしょう。そして、少女時代のあの幸福な夏の日々を懐かしみ、思いを馳せることでしょう。

【解説】不思議の国に迷いこんだアリスは、偉そうで自己中心的な者や、哀れでおかし

覚えておきたい英語表現

い動物たち、すーっと見え隠れする反骨精神に富んだネコなど、個性豊かな登場人物たちと出会います。みんな、会話の主導権を握り、アリスがまじめに会話しようとしても、なかなかうまくいきません。わけのわからないことを言われたり、一方的に会話を中断されたり、ぶっきらぼうな対応をしたかと思うと、アリスを無視して、好きなだけ黙り込んでしまう者もいます。

ことばの意味のみを知っていても、相手とつながる会話の仕方を知らないか、するつもりもない連中が、次々と登場するのです。それでもアリスは、いつも一生懸命、真摯に、相手と心を通わせようとけなげな努力をします。

> She would understand all their sadnesses and find happinesses in all their joys.
> 子供たちが抱くせつない思いを受けとめ、子供たちの喜びに心震わせることでしょう。

これは、アリスが人生で一番大切なことを学んだことを表わしています。心を触れ合わせるためには、相手とつながる言葉を使い、相手の思いに共感して聞くことが大切だということを学んだのです。現実社会も、難しい言葉を乱発して、何を言いたいのかまったくわからない"偉い人"たちや、心を通わせることができない、あるいは、心を通わせることには無関心な人がたくさんいます。

今私たちが住んでいる世界は、不思議の国かもしれません。だからこそ、一人でも多くの人とつながる努力をして、相手を思いやるコミュニケーションを成立させることに努めなくてはならないのです。

アリスが不思議の国で経験したこと――ことばを使っても相手と"つながる"ことができないせつなさや、哀しさを知ったアリスは、きっと、賢くて思いやりにあふれる、素晴らしい女性になることでしょう。

and she would understand は、「きっとわかってあげられるでしょう」の意味。相手に対する理解と共感を表わすときに使います。wouldを入れることによって、「理解しようと努める」というニュアンスが出ます。

【例文】① If you must go, I would understand.
あなたが行ってしまっても、だいじょうぶ、心配しないで。(意訳)

＊相手の意思を尊重し、自分のことを気遣わなくてもよいので安心して、と言っています。(本音はわかりませんが…？)そう言われたら、去りがたくなる？

② I would understand why you must disagree.
君が反対する理由(わけ)は、理解できるよ。

Free Space

● E-CATとは…
英語が話せるようになるためのテストです。インターネットベースで、30分であなたの発話力をチェックします。

www.ecatexam.com

● iTEP®とは…
世界各国の企業、政府機関、アメリカの大学300校以上が、英語能力判定テストとして採用。オンラインによる90分のテストで文法、リーディング、リスニング、ライティング、スピーキングの5技能をスコア化。iTEP®は、留学、就職、海外赴任などに必要な、世界に通用する英語力を総合的に評価する画期的なテストです。

www.itepexamjapan.com

[IBC対訳ライブラリー]
英語で読む不思議の国のアリス

2012年8月5日　第1刷発行
2019年8月11日　第5刷発行

原　著　者　ルイス・キャロル
翻訳・解説　井上　久美

発行者　浦　晋亮
発行所　IBCパブリッシング株式会社
　　　　〒162-0804 東京都新宿区中里町29番3号 菱秀神楽坂ビル9F
　　　　Tel. 03-3513-4511　Fax. 03-3513-4512
　　　　www.ibcpub.co.jp

印刷所　株式会社シナノパブリッシングプレス
CDプレス　株式会社ケーエヌコーポレーションジャパン

© IBC Publishing, Inc. 2012

Printed in Japan

落丁本・乱丁本は、小社宛にお送りください。送料小社負担にてお取り替えいたします。
本書の無断複写（コピー）は著作権法上の例外を除き禁じられています。

ISBN978-4-7946-0157-5